# Pocket Pal®

A Graphic Arts Production Handbook

SO-ABM-552

Thirteenth Edition

INTERNATIONAL PAPER COMPANY

First Edition – 1934
Second Edition – September 1938
Third Edition – October 1954
Fourth Edition – November 1955
Fifth Edition – October 1957
Sixth Edition – April 1960
Seventh Edition – June 1963
Eighth Edition – November 1964
Ninth Edition – February 1966
Tenth Edition – May 1970
Eleventh Edition – December 1974
Twelfth Edition – March 1979
Thirteenth Edition – May 1983
Second Printing – January 1984

Copyright© 1963, 1964, 1966, 1970, 1974, 1979, 1983
by
INTERNATIONAL PAPER COMPANY
International Paper Plaza
77 West 45th Street
New York, NY 10036
All Rights Reserved

# foreword

Ever since its debut in 1934, the Pocket Pal has served as an authoritative introduction to the graphic arts for many artists, designers, advertisers, students and buyers of printing. Acclaimed by many authorities as the best publication of its type, Pocket Pal is now in its 13th Edition as International Paper Company has continually strived to keep its content accurate and current.

At the time of Pocket Pal's first edition, the term *printing* was associated predominantly with *letterpress*, and the other processes, *lithography*, *gravure*, and *screen printing*, were subordinate to letterpress used mainly for special purposes or to imitate letterpress at lower cost. In the almost fifty years since the first edition, the situation has changed drastically. Now the word *printing* no longer is used to refer solely to letterpress but encompasses all the graphic arts processes. In fact, letterpress's dominance has gradually given way to lithography in commercial, book, newspaper and magazine printing, while gravure has made sizable gains in catalog printing, publishing, packaging and other specialty areas, and *flexography* has become the leading relief process expanding into other areas besides packaging.

In the 10th Edition, the format of the Pocket Pal was changed to present each of the printing processes in its proper perspective. Each new edition has incorporated the many changes and developments that have occurred since the previous one and has assessed their effects on the future of the printing industry. This edition features the many changes occurring in printing with the widespread introduction and use of electronics and the computer. It contains two new sections that describe the new technology and its developments: *electronic pre-press systems* and *quality control*.

Michael H. Bruno
Graphic Arts Consultant,
Editor

# Contents

# History

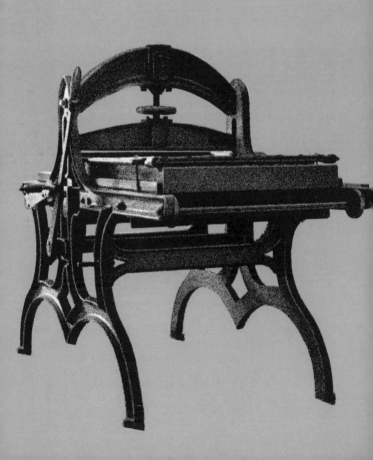

## INTRODUCTION

Printing is something which can be seen, perceived with our eyes and reproduced in quantity. Regardless of the great number and variety of printed products they all have one thing in common: *each has the same visible image produced in quantity.*

Printing and publishing is a big business in the U.S.A. which altogether represents about 3% of the gross national product (GNP). Among all U.S. manufacturing industries, the most recent statistics rank it first in the total number of establishments — almost 50,000 — with 80% having less than 20 employees. Of the more than $81.6 billion of shipments of printing and publishing products in 1982, *commercial printing* accounted for $23.9 billion; *newspaper* and *magazine* production was over $32.5 billion, *book publishing* and *printing* was $9.8 billion. These figures do not include packaging, in-plant and quick printing.

Today's printer owes much to the Age of Science, particularly to electronics, computers, chemistry, optics and mechanics. Modern printing is becoming highly sophisticated. As new presses, inks, papers, plastics, electronic scanners, lasers, and computer programs are developed and other products of modern science and research are applied to printing, it is gradually being transformed from an art to a science.

## THE EVOLUTION OF PRINTING

Man's earliest known attempt at a visual record of his life and times dates back 30,000 years. These were wall drawings called pictographs, superseded by the more complex ideographs. They in turn were succeeded by the Persians' cuneiforms, and then by hieroglyphics, perfected by the Egyptians around 2500 B.C. Ten centuries later the Phoenicians used the first formal alphabet. But these are art forms and not printing as it is usually defined.

Evidence of the first example of printing from movable type was discovered in 1908 by an Italian archaeologist on the island of Crete. He found a clay disc in the ruins of the palace of Phaistos in a stratification dated about 1500 B.C.

Printing from movable type appeared in China and Korea in the 11th century. In 1041, a Chinese, Pi-Sheng, developed type characters from hardened clay. They were not wholly successful. Type cast from metal in Korea was widely used in China and Japan, and by the middle 1200s type characters were being cast in bronze. The oldest text known was printed from such type in Korea in 1397 A.D.

Half a century later in 1440, probably unaware of the crude type developed in the Orient, Johann Gutenberg brought the West up to date with his invention of movable type. Until Gutenberg's system of separate characters for printing on a press with ink on paper, all books were laboriously handwritten by scribes. Little wonder that historians credit his invention as the beginning of printing, coinciding with the end of the Middle Ages and the beginning of the Renaissance and Modern History.

Paper and printing ink were not new when Gutenberg's type appeared. The use of parchment was introduced for writing by Eumenes, king of Pergamus, in 170 B.C. Two hundred years later, Wang Ch'ung, a Chinese philosopher, used bamboo as a writing surface. Another Chinese, Ts'ai Lun, is credited with the invention of paper in 105 A.D. By the time Gutenberg was born, papermaking was a well-developed industry throughout the Western hemisphere with paper mills existing in Spain, France, Italy and Germany.

In making ink for printing, the Chinese also led the world in discovery. Wei Tang perfected an ink for block printing using lampblack in 400 A.D. Viscous or tacky inks, essential to printing, were already in use in Germany for block printing and for stamping titles on manuscript bookbindings by Gutenberg's time.

To Gutenberg we must credit the envisionment of commercial and cultural possibilities of printing as a process of graphic reproduction. To the cumulative effect of inventions of many minds in a growing civilization, we must attribute the evolution of printing as a graphic art.

## TYPE BEGINNINGS

Our common type faces are either imitations of early handwritten letters or represent a modification of early type faces which, in turn, were modeled after the lettering in manuscript books.

The standard *roman* lower-case letters and capitals assumed their present form about 1470 in a face cut by Nicolas Jenson. While Jenson, a Frenchman, learned printing in Germany, he did his first printing in Venice, Italy. The letters inscribed in manuscript books by Venetian monks were Jenson's models. His types served as a pattern for later faces. Jenson was not the first to use roman letters, but he must receive credit for developing a beautiful face upon which no later designer has been able to improve significantly. Type faces similar to Jenson are often called Venetian types.

The first books in Europe were printed in black-letter or *gothic* type. They were designed to imitate the style of letter used by religious scribes living in the vicinity of Mainz, Germany, where Gutenberg began his printing activities. John Fust and Peter Schoeffer, who entered the printing field through business relations with Gutenberg, continued to use the gothic letter form. Thus, it became firmly established in Northern Europe.

To avoid confusion, it must be pointed out that the term "gothic," as used by some modern typefounders to designate sans serif types, has no relation to gothic as a description of early type faces. Gothic, as a term applied to architecture and other forms of art, designates the style characteristic of Northern and Western Europe from the twelfth to sixteenth century. It is in this sense that gothic is also applied to letter forms.

SETTING TYPE BY HAND          EARLY TYPE FACES

Roman Type

**a**

Gothic Type

**𝖆**

## ROMAN LETTER DEVELOPMENT

The manuscript hand of the Venetian scribes, which Nicolas Jenson followed as his model, developed apart from gothic lettering. It had evolved from roman capital letters. In formal writing and inscriptions the early Romans used square capitals, with slight modifications, in the form of our upper-case alphabet. For correspondence and documents not requiring formal writing, large cursive or running capitals were used.

Many national styles in writing developed as learning was carried from Rome throughout the rest of the known world. The influence of the roman characters might have been lost, however, had not Emperor Charlemagne taken an interest in the revival and spread of ancient learning. Charlemagne encouraged the establishment of a school at Tours by an English scholar named Alcuin. The calligraphy of this school became the model for the rest of Europe.

By the tenth century the use of letter forms from which we derive our lower case was quite universal. However, these letters did not assume the fixed form with which we are familiar until they were cast in type by Jenson.

## ITALICS AND DISPLAY TYPES

Practically all roman type faces in common use today have accompanying *italics*. This was not true of early roman faces. Jenson, for example, did not produce *cursive* type; italics were a separate development.

Italics were first used to print small, compact books. Early books were large and cumbersome, for gothic type used in these books was large. When roman type came into use, it was cast smaller than gothic, and letters and lines were fitted more closely. But even this economy in page size did not satisfy Aldus Manutius, a Venetian printer around the turn of the fifteenth century. Sensing a growing trend for cheaper books, he tried to meet the demand by cutting a font of type to imitate the informal handwriting of his time. Aldus called this type *Chancery;* his Italian contemporaries called it *Aldine;* but in the rest of Europe, the face was called *italic.* This latter designation has continued in use to the present time.

Display types of today are difficult to trace historically. All were derived from hand-drawn letters. They may have been specifically drawn as a type-design or developed from a letter drawn for another purpose.

## EARLY PRINTING IN ENGLAND

We are interested in early printing in England because it was through England that printing came to the American colonies. Printing was introduced in England about 1476 by William Caxton, who brought equipment from the Netherlands to establish a press at Westminster. Among the books issued from Caxton's press were Chaucer's *The Canterbury Tales, Fables of Aesop,* and many other popular works.

The predecessor of the modern Oxford University Press was established in 1585. Since that date the press has operated continuously, probably the longest period of any printing establishment in history.

Richard Pynson, who printed in England during the latter part of the fifteenth and early sixteenth centuries, is believed to have been the first to introduce roman types in England. John Day, who began printing on his own account in 1546, was the first English designer of a roman type face.

## TWO FAMOUS ENGLISH TYPE DESIGNERS

William Caslon, born in 1692 in Worcestershire, was destined to change the appearance of English printing through the design and casting of a new type face. Not only is Caslon type still used, but his style of printing is still consciously or unconsciously followed by many contemporary typographers. An axiom of printers with a type problem is, "When in doubt, use Caslon!" Although Caslon's letters are not perfect in themselves, a page of Caslon type produces a simple, pleasing and balanced effect.

The English printer and typographer, John Baskerville, born in 1706, is regarded by some students of the history of printing as the father of fine printing in England. Baskerville, after having accumulated a fair-sized fortune in other fields, established a paper mill, printing office and type foundry at Birmingham in 1750. Baskerville spent several years experimenting with designs for type. He also tried to improve the surface of sheets of paper by pressing them between hot plates after printing, and he mixed special inks which were used in producing his first book. Consequently, when he offered his first printed works to the public around 1757, they gained wide acclaim.

The types designed by Baskerville are usually considered to represent a halfway step between the *old-style* roman letter which Caslon so clearly exemplified and the *modern* style of roman letter which is best illustrated by the face developed by the Italian printer, Bodoni.

While England's contribution to the development of printing was not as great as that of countries in Continental Europe, it was through English printers that the early traditions of printing in America were established.

## EARLY PRINTING IN AMERICA

Printing was used to promote colonization of the New World. There is on file in the New York Public Library a copy of such a promotion piece dated 1609. It is entitled, "Offering Most Excellent Fruites by Planting in Virginia." One historian, observing the fact that 750 of the first 900 settlers in the Virginia Colonies died during the first winter, marvels at the force of the printed word. It not only induced new settlers to come to the New World, but also influenced the 150 survivors to remain.

The extent to which printing was used in promoting the New England Colonies is not known. The first printing press made its appearance in Massachusetts in 1638, soon after the first settlers established themselves. The first piece printed on the new press was *The Freeman's Oath.* The *Bay Psalm Book,* eleven copies of which are still in existence, was produced in 1640. It was printed on an early colonial press procured in England by Reverend Jose Glover who died on the voyage to America, but his wife assumed responsibility for setting up the press in Cambridge. Stephen Daye, who had been indentured by the

Reverend Glover to operate the press, was placed in charge and, with his son, Matthew, continued its operation until 1647.

In the meantime, Glover's widow was married again, this time to President Dunster of Harvard College. Upon her death the press was moved to Harvard and used in close association with the college. In a sense, this represents the beginning of Harvard University Press, the oldest continuously operated printing activity in America.

Printing did not make headway in the southern colonies to the extent that it did in the Massachusetts Colony. By 1770 there were at least a dozen printers in Boston. By 1763 there was a press in operation in Georgia, the last of the thirteen colonies to be settled. Printing came to Kentucky, Tennessee, Ohio and Michigan in the 1780s and 1790s. In 1808 printing had moved west of the Mississippi to St. Louis. Thus, as migration continued west, printing followed.

## TWO PRINTER PATRIOTS

Benjamin Franklin, believed by some to have been the most important American citizen of his time, was born in Boston in 1706. As a boy he learned printing in the shop of his brother. In 1723 he quarrelled with his brother and went to New York. Unable to find work he continued on to Philadelphia where he worked for a French printer named Keimer.

At the suggestion of the governor of Pennsylvania, Sir William Keith, young Franklin went to England to buy a printing outfit. Money which he had been promised was not forthcoming, so for two years he worked in famous English printing plants, including that of William Watts. In 1726 he returned to Philadelphia. By 1732 he had his own printing office and became the publisher of the *Pennsylvania Gazette*. Among his publications, *Poor Richard's Almanack* became the most famous.

Throughout his life, Franklin was active in promoting printing. Although he disposed of his business in Philadelphia in 1748 to devote his time to literary, journalistic and civic activities, he assisted in the establishment and promotion of forty or more printing plants in the Colonies. Franklin's high regard for his craft is revealed by the words with which he began his will: ''I, Benjamin Franklin, Printer . . .''

Franklin is not the only printer of the Revolutionary Period who is celebrated as a great patriot. There are several; outstanding among them is Isaiah Thomas. Thomas, born in Massachusetts in 1744, was actively engaged in printing early in his life. In 1770 he began publication of the *Massachusetts Spy*, a newspaper in which he supported the cause of the patriots. He served during the Revolutionary War as printer for the Massachusetts House of Assembly. Following the war, he re-established his business which had been destroyed. As a printer he prospered and became the leading publisher of books in the period following the Revolution. In 1810 he published a two-volume *History of Printing in America* which, even today, remains the best source on colonial printing.

## TYPE AND TYPECASTING MACHINES

For more than four hundred years after the invention of printing, all type was set by hand. In the nineteenth century, men began to consider the possibility of creating typesetting machines. Numerous machines intended to replace hand composition were invented. The first of these was designed by an Englishman, Dr. William Church, in 1822; others soon followed. While many of the first typesetting machines functioned satisfactorily, none were sufficiently practical for commercial operation until the invention of the linotype by Ottmar Mergenthaler in 1886.

CHURCH'S TYPESETTING MACHINE

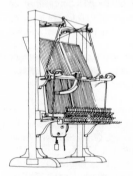

Of the various metal composing machines developed, only two kinds are still in use. These are machines such as the Linotype, Intertype, and Ludlow which cast *slugs* (one-piece fully spaced lines); and the Monotype which casts *individual pieces of type* in justified lines.

The Monotype was invented in 1887 by Tolbert Lanston of Washington, D.C. The Ludlow Typograph was suggested by Washington I. Ludlow in 1906 and later perfected by William A. Reade. Intertype, a later development in 1911, utilized the Mergenthaler principle. The most recent development in machine composition is photographic typesetting.

## PLATEMAKING BEFORE PHOTOGRAPHY

The first illustrations in books were made from woodcuts. They were tooled out of wood blocks by hand, leaving raised surfaces. The earliest known book using woodcuts was printed by Albrecht Pfister in Bamberg about 1460.

Books printed between 1570 and 1770 were usually illustrated by copperplate engravings, resulting in a decline in the making of woodcuts. In 1770, however, a revival was started by Thomas Bewick of England who developed the technique of using a special engraving tool for cutting *across* the grain, instead of *with* the grain. Today, woodcuts are used only to give an "artistic touch" to certain types of printed pieces.

Engraved copper intaglio plates, the forerunner of steel engravings and gravure, were first used in France and Italy around 1476. Copper engraving offered competition to woodcuts in England about 1545, and in France about 1569. Copperplate work has continued to be practiced through the years and is still used for invitations and announcements.

## PHOTOGRAPHY AND PHOTOMECHANICS

Photography for graphic arts involves the photographic processes and techniques used to reproduce illustrations and art subjects; photomechanics or photoplatemaking, like photoengraving, photolithography, photogelatin, photogravure, etc., is the means of using the products of photography like halftone and line films to make plates and cylinders for printing. The invention and use of photography and photomechanics completed the mechanization of the printing process; made illustrations practical and economical to produce and reproduce; and fostered the phenomenal growth of advertising, periodical, book and commercial printing.

The blackening effect of light on silver salts had been known by alchemists for years but it was not until 1839 — a banner year for photography — that methods were developed to use the phenomenon to produce permanent images. Daguerre is usually credited with the invention of the first practical process of photography, but in the same year, the astronomer Herschel, who had discovered the fixing properties of sodium thiosulfate (hypo) in 1819, gave the process the name "photography" and Fox Talbot invented the first negative-positive process called Calotype, which eventually proved more practical than Daguerre's process. In 1851 F. Scott Archer invented the wet collodion process of photography which remained in use until the middle of the 20th century. Many other improvements were made in the 50 years between Fox Talbot's Calotype process and 1889 when George Eastman introduced the first flexible film base and the Kodak camera and photography exploded! Improvements continued and culminated in 1929 with the introduction of the first high contrast lith film, Kodalith, and in 1936 with Kodachrome — the first multilayer color film — invented by two musicians, Mannes and Godowsky.

The development of photomechanics closely paralleled the advances in photography. In 1826 Joseph Niepce, Daguerre's partner, made the first metal engraving by light using a metal plate coated with bitumen and etched after exposure and development. In 1839 Ponton discovered the use of potassium bichromate as a sensitizer, and in 1852 Fox Talbot used it to sensitize gelatin and produced the first halftone engraving by laying a screen of fine gauze between the coated metal and a negative of the original picture. This is the first known use of the screen principle which created the "dot pattern" as it is known today. In 1855 Poitevin invented photolithography based on bichromated albumin.

Photoengraving developed rapidly in America, and by 1871 it was commercially practicable for letterpress printing. By 1880 photoengraved prints were replacing woodcuts as illustrations in books and magazines. In that year, Stephen Horgan made the first halftone photoengraving for printing. It utilized a coarse screen and was printed by lithography in *The Daily Graphic* of New York, the first picture newspaper.

The first commercial halftone screen was produced in 1883 by Max and Louis Levy of Philadelphia. Two years later Frederick Ives improved on their technique by developing the earliest version of the glass crossline screen. Although the first halftones were black and white, the application of halftones to color process printing was not long in developing. Color process work was successfully printed in 1893, and today is one of the most widely used methods of graphic reproduction.

## DEVELOPMENT OF THE PRINTING PRESS

In hand composition there is much in common between printing today and printing as it was practiced by the followers of Gutenberg. The general appearance of type, its casting, and the procedures used in putting it together to form words, lines and pages have not radically changed.

In transferring the impression to paper by the use of printing presses, however, radical changes have occurred. The crude wooden hand presses of the early printers, capable of turning out 300 to 500 sheets in a day, have been replaced with power driven machines which produce the same number of impressions in a few minutes (in newspaper printing, a few seconds).

Benjamin Franklin worked on a wooden-frame press in the printing office of William Watts in London. This press used a torsion screw for making the impression and was provided with a clever mechanical arrangement devised to provide the proper pressure on the form. This was an improvement over the Stephen Daye press, which was brought to Cambridge from London in 1638. Further changes in press construction came

STEPHEN DAYE PRESS

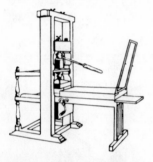

about slowly until the first all-metal press was built by the Earl of Stanhope early in the nineteenth century. This press still used a screw device, but less exertion was required to force the impression on the sheet. Application of the principle of the lever to the iron press resulted in several presses which came into common use. Among these were the Columbian Press, built by George Clymer of New York; the Albion Press, invented by R.W. Cope of London; and the Washington Press, perfected by Samuel Rust. The Washington Press became popular in the United States, and by 1900 over 6,000 had been sold. The Albion Press was equally popular in England.

The idea of the printing press, as conceived by Gutenberg, reached its highest development in the Washington and Albion Presses. The modern job press and the cylinder press are distinctly different machines. However, the first power press did have some of the features of the hand presses. The Adams Press, patented by Isaac Adams in 1830, raised and lowered the form by means of a steam-powered cam, which operated a toggle joint. In appearance, the Adams Press has been described as ''an old-fashioned hand press turned upside down.''

The job, or platen, press is the direct descendant of a machine perfected in 1858 by George P. Gordon of New York. In this machine the platen and form are turned on edge. Of the models manufactured today, some employ a rigid bed, with the platen drawn up against the form. In others, both the platen and bed move with a sort of clamshell action.

The cylinder press was first conceived by William Nicholson of London who secured patents in 1790 but was unable to perfect a working model. The first steam-powered cylinder press was built in London under the supervision of a German named Frederick König, who seemed to have known something of Nicholson's ideas. It was used for printing *The London Times* in 1814 and was capable of producing 1,100 sheets per hour. A rotating cylinder was used to press the paper against a flat type bed.

Most flat-bed cylinder presses trace back to König's first cylinder machine. Shortly after König's press was placed in operation in 1814, D. Napier, an Englishman, invented a press using grippers for picking up the sheet from the paper table and holding it while the sheet received the impression.

HOE'S TEN-CYLINDER PRESS

Numerous other improvements have been added throughout the years, and while most present-day cylinder presses produce up to 5,000 impressions per hour, they are gradually becoming obsolete. No flat-bed cylinder presses, except the vertical press, are produced in the U.S. anymore.

In the United States, Richard Hoe perfected the first rotary press in 1847, with the type actually carried on the cylinder. Early models produced 2,000 impressions per hour per cylinder.

The first web press was developed by an American, William Bullock, in 1856. A similar press was patented ten years later in London. These early presses delivered 15,000 signatures per hour printed both sides. A device for folding the papers as they came from the press was added in 1875.

Since that time newspaper presses have been developed to a high state of efficiency which, by duplicating plates and units, has allowed newspapers to be printed and delivered at the rate of 160,000 per hour.

## DISCOVERY OF LITHOGRAPHY

The basic principle of lithography, "writing on stone," was discovered by Alois Senefelder of Munich around 1798. Working on a highly porous stone, he sketched his design with a greasy substance which was absorbed by the stone. He then wetted the entire surface with a mixture of gum arabic and water. Only the blank areas absorbed the solution; the design area repelled it. Rolling on an ink made of soap, wax, oil and lampblack, this substance, being greasy, coated the design but did not spread over the moist blank area. A clean impression of the design was then made when a sheet of paper was pressed against the surface of the stone.

SENEFELDER'S PRESS

Artists soon used this new process to make reproductions of the works of old masters and, in time, recognized it as a valuable medium for their own original works. It received its biggest boost towards recognition when Currier and Ives popularized lithography in the middle of the 19th century. This new recognition and popularity encouraged printers to find more practical and faster methods using the principle of lithography.

The first American steam press for lithography was designed by R. Hoe of New York about 1868. Stones transferred the image; the "steam" operated an engine that drove the press, just as an electric motor does now.

In 1906 the first "offset" press as we know it today began rolling out printed sheets in Nutley, New Jersey, an invention of Ira A.

Rubel, a paper manufacturer. Actually the discovery was an accident. An impression was unintentionally printed from a press cylinder directly onto the rubber blanket of the impression cylinder. Immediately afterwards, when a sheet of paper was run through the press, a sharp image was printed on it from the impression which had been "offset" on the rubber blanket. A.F. Harris had noticed a similar effect, and he too developed an offset press for the Harris Automatic Press Company of Niles, Ohio, in the same year, 1906.

## HISTORY OF PRINTING PAPERS

As already stated papermaking was invented in China over 1800 years ago. By 1200 A.D. paper was being made in Spain, and 200 years later the art was well established throughout Europe. The first paper mill in England was built in 1494. In the American colonies, paper was first manufactured commercially in 1690, in a mill near Philadelphia owned by William Rittenhouse. Paper originally was made for uses other than printing; but the invention of the printing press resulted in many changes in the products of paper mills and the methods of making them.

Ancient papers were made almost entirely from rags and were produced with crude hand-operated devices. Most papers currently used in printing are manufactured from wood pulp. A few writing and ledger papers are still made from rags, but even these contain a percentage of wood pulp.

The machine for producing a continuous web of paper was invented by a Frenchman, Louis Robert, in 1798. His invention was financed and developed by an English family, the Fourdriniers, and even today, a papermaking machine is referred to as a "Fourdrinier."

The manufacturing of paper from mechanical groundwood pulp was introduced to the world in 1840. Production of cellulose, or wood fibre, by chemical methods, using caustic soda, was perfected in 1854. The use of bisulphite of lime, in the chemical production of pulp, came into use about 1866. Recently thermomechanical pulping was developed and now all three pulps are widely used for the manufacture of paper.

## HISTORY OF PRINTING INKS

No history of printing would be complete without some mention of the history of inkmaking. As stated at the start of this section, ink was already in use for printing from wood blocks at the time Gutenberg developed his movable type system. Actually, the origin of printing ink is shrouded in mystery. It developed from writing ink which was used by the Egyptians and Chinese as early as 2600 B.C. These early inks consisted of lampblack or soot mixed with animal glue or vegetable oils. Inkmaking became a highly developed art among the Chinese as they introduced earth colors and printed from hand cut blocks in the 11th century — 400 years before Gutenberg.

In the early days the printer made his own inks using lampblack and boiled linseed oil which he cooked according to his own "secret" formula. Inkmaking developed on a commercial scale in the 16th and 17th centuries. The first ink factory was established in America in 1742. Little color was used until the discovery of coal tar dyes in the middle of the nineteenth century. Now inkmaking has been highly refined with special inks for each process and purpose, and represents a more than one billion dollar industry in the U.S. alone.

## THE PRESENT

While Gutenberg did well to produce a single one-color impression in three minutes, some of today's rotary presses print multicolor on both sides of a continuous roll of paper at speeds over 2500 feet or 1000 printed signatures per minute! And yet, if Gutenberg or his contemporaries had stepped into the average printing plant in 1950, they could have stood at a typecase, set type by hand and pulled a proof almost exactly as they did when printing was invented over 500 years earlier. Not any more. They might recognize the output, but the input would be completely strange to them.

The age of electronics and the computer has completely changed the complexion of the printing processes. In the 30 years since 1950, not only have presses been speeded up, but most hand and machine composition has been replaced by photo and computer typesetting; photography is controlled by densitometers, exposure computers and automatic processors; most color separations and corrections are done electronically on scanners, and halftone output films are generated by lasers; some stripping is done by computer aided design (CAD) techniques; plates are processed automatically and some are being exposed directly from pasteups by lasers without any intermediate films; ink fountains are being pre-set on presses automatically from data derived from scanning the printing plates before mounting on the press; computers are being used to analyze production information on presses; and bindery lines are being operated almost automatically by computers for some magazine printing.

These advances and improvements, along with the conventional methods have made printing a mature combination of processes and techniques which make up much of the subject matter of the succeeding chapters in the *Pocket Pal*.

## THE FUTURE

The future of the printing processes is being shaped by the expansive versatility and capabilities of the microcomputer and microprocessor. Systems are being developed for making printing plates and/or cylinders directly from original copy without any intermediate photography or film. Printing is entering a filmless era, and printing without plates by jet and electronic printing will increase. More importantly, printers and publishers are beginning to realize that they are a part of the vast information industry that employs over two-thirds of the work force in the U.S., and many are already looking at other information processing systems like telecommunications, videotex, interactive cable TV, direct broadcast by satellite, etc., as complements or supplements to printing.

While printing is sure to change more in the next 20 years than it has in the more than 500 years since Gutenberg, contrary to the predictions of McLuhan and other prophets of doom, the printed word will survive and continue to flourish well into the 21st century. It is certain to change in the way it is composed and produced, but it will be around for many years for people to read, admire and enjoy.

# The printing processes

Four major processes are used in printing: letterpress, gravure, offset-lithography, and screen. Each uses a different method: letterpress is *relief,* gravure is *intaglio,* lithography is *planographic,* and screen is *porous* or *stencil* printing. Some office duplicating and electrostatic printing processes use modifications of these methods.

At present the distribution of these processes for printing, publishing and packaging, excluding copying and duplicating, are: lithography 44%; gravure 18%; letterpress 18%; flexography 14%; screen printing and other processes 6%. By 1990, the use of these processes is expected to be as follows: lithography 46%; gravure 22%; flexography 18%; screen printing and other processes 9%; letterpress 5%.

LETTERPRESS (Relief)          GRAVURE (Intaglio)

OFFSET (Planographic)          SCREEN (Porous or Stencil)

## LETTERPRESS

This is the oldest and most versatile method of printing. There is equipment for short, medium or long runs; it is used for job and commercial printing, books, newspapers, magazines, as well as packaging printing and many types of specialty printing.

Letterpress is printed by the *relief* method. It is the only process which can use type directly. Printing is done from cast metal type or plates on which the image or printing areas are raised above the non-printing areas. Ink rollers touch only the top surface of the raised areas; the surrounding (non-printing) areas are lower and do not receive ink. The inked image is transferred directly to the paper.

Inasmuch as letterpress is the only process where printing is done directly from type, this makes it economical for jobs consisting mainly of reading matter such as price lists, parts lists, directories, rate schedules, timetables and legal work. Changes can be readily made, and the type can be kept 'standing', ready to be used again for reprints. The convenience of typesetting by cast metal, however, is rapidly giving way to photo and computer typesetting.

Much time is consumed in *makeready* (building up of the press form so that both the light and heavy areas print with the correct impression). When highlights and shadows are at the same height, the highlights exert more pressure than the shadows so that pressure must be relieved in the highlights and more pressure added in the shadows or heavy printing areas.

There are four types of presses: platen, flat-bed cylinder, rotary and belt, described in detail on pages 128-130. On platen and flat-bed cylinder presses, the type or plates are mounted on a flat surface or bed. Type and flat plates cannot be used on rotary presses, where the printing member is a cylinder, and plates must be curved.

Printing is done on sheets of paper on sheet-fed presses, or rolls of paper on web-fed presses. Sheet-fed letterpress on small platen and flat-bed cylinder presses is used for short run printing such as letterheads, billheads, envelopes, announcements, invitations, and small advertising brochures. Larger sheet-fed letterpress is used for general printing, books, catalogs, advertising, and packaging. Web letterpress is used for newspapers and magazines.

The distinctive feature for recognizing letterpress is a heavier edge of ink around each letter (seen with a magnifying glass). The ink tends to spread slightly from the pressure of the plate upon the printed surface. Sometimes a slight embossing (be-

HOW TO RECOGNIZE THE PRINTING PROCESSES

| LETTERPRESS | GRAVURE | OFFSET |
|---|---|---|
| (Ring of Ink) | (Serrated Edges) | (Smooth Edges) |

cause of denting) appears on the reverse side of the paper. The letterpress image is usually sharp and crisp.

## Flexography

Flexography is a form of rotary web letterpress using flexible rubber plates and fast-drying solvent or water-based inks. The rubber plates are mounted to the printing cylinder with double-faced adhesive. Plates are sometimes backed with thin brass or other metal sheets and attached to the cylinder with fastening straps for close register.

Most anything that can go through a web press can be printed by flexography. Printing by the flexographic process ranges from decorated toilet tissue to bags, corrugated board and materials such as foil, hard-calendered papers, cellophane, polyethylene and other plastic films. It is well suited for printing large areas of solid color. Inks can be overlaid to obtain high gloss and special effects.

The growth of flexography parallels the expansion of the packaging industry, the development of the central impression cylinder press, new ink metering systems and new photopolymer plates. Halftones as fine as 150 lines per inch can be printed on flexible films. It is also gaining prominence in the printing of business forms, books, folding cartons and corrugated boxes, as well as many specialty items from drinking straws to shower curtains. It is the major process for printing milk containers. Because of its color brilliance, flexography is used extensively in printing gift wraps and shopping bags. The improved quality of photopolymer plates and controlled inking of the new ink metering systems have introduced flexography to newspaper and magazine printing. It is also used extensively for heat transfer printing *(see page 138)*.

## Thermography (Raised Printing)

Thermography is a process which creates special embossed effects in printing such as stationery, invitations, greeting cards, and paper decoration. A raised surface of printing resembling die engraving is formed without using costly engraving dies. Special non-drying inks are used in printing, either by letterpress or offset, and the wet inks are dusted with a powdered compound. After the excess powder on the non-printing areas is removed by suction, the sheet passes under a heater which fuses the ink and powdered compound. The printing swells or *raises* in relief to produce a pleasing engraved effect.

## GRAVURE

Gravure is an example of intaglio printing. It uses a sunken or *depressed* surface for the image. The image areas consist of cells or wells etched into a copper cylinder or wraparound plate, and the cylinder or plate surface represents the non-printing areas. The plate cylinder rotates in a bath of ink. The excess is wiped off the surface by a flexible steel *doctor blade*. The ink remaining in the thousands of recessed cells forms the image by direct transfer to the paper as it passes between the plate cylinder and the impression cylinder.

Gravure printing is considered to be excellent for reproducing pictures, but high plate-making expense usually limits its use to long runs. A distinctive feature for recognizing gravure is that the entire image is screened — type and line drawings — as well as halftones. The usual gravure screen is 150 lines per inch, virtually invisible to the naked eye.

PRINCIPLE OF GRAVURE

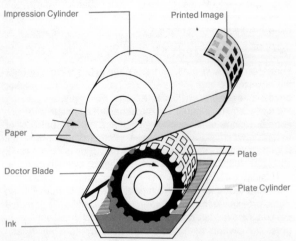

There are three types of gravure: conventional, variable area-variable depth, and direct transfer or variable area. These are described on pages 123-124. Conventional gravure is used for shorter run, high quality illustration printing. Variable area-variable depth is used for newspaper supplement, magazine and catalog printing. Variable area gravure is used mainly for packaging printing.

As with rotary letterpress, gravure presses are manufactured to print sheets (sheet-fed gravure) or rolls (rotogravure) of paper, but most gravure is printed from rolls. Sunday newspaper magazine sections or supplements, color preprints for newspapers, large mail order catalogs, wallpaper, plastic laminates and postage stamps are examples of rotogravure printing.

## Steel-Die Engraving

Steel-die engraving is an intaglio process in which the die is hand or machine cut, or chemically etched to hold ink. The plate is inked so that all sub-surfaces are filled with ink. Then the surface is wiped clean, leaving ink only in the depressed (or sunken) areas of the plate. The paper is slightly moistened and forced against the plate with tremendous pressure, drawing the ink from the depressed areas. This produces the characteristic embossed surface, with a slightly indented impression on the back of the paper.

Copper plates are used for short runs of one-time use (invitations and announcements). For longer or repeat runs such as letterheads, envelopes, greeting cards, stamps, money, and stock certificates, chromium-plated copper or steel plates are used in a die-stamping press.

## OFFSET LITHOGRAPHY

The most popular of the four major printing processes, lithography, uses the *planographic* method. The image and non-printing areas are essentially on the same plane of a thin metal plate, and the distinction between them is maintained chemically. Printing is from a *plane* or flat surface, and there are two basic differences between offset lithography and other processes: (1) it is based on the principle that grease and water do not mix, and (2) ink is *offset* first from the plate to a rubber blanket, and then from the blanket to the paper.

When the printing plate is made, the printing image is rendered grease receptive and water repellent, while the non-printing areas are rendered water receptive and ink repellent. On the press the plate is mounted on the plate cylinder which, as it rotates, comes into contact successively with rollers wet by a water or dampening solution, and rollers wet by ink. The dampening solution wets the non-printing areas of the plate and prevents the ink from wetting these areas. The ink wets the image areas which are transferred to the intermediate blanket cylinder. The paper picks up the image as it passes between the blanket cylinder and the impression cylinder.

Transferring the image from the plate to a rubber blanket before transfer to the paper is called the *offset principle*. Letterpress and gravure can also be printed by this offset principle. But because most lithography is printed in this way, the term *offset* has become synonymous with lithography.

One major advantage of the offset principle is that the soft rubber surface of the blanket creates a clearer impression on a wide variety of paper surfaces and other materials with both rough and smooth textures with a minimum of press makeready. Offset printing can be recognized by a smooth print, as well as by the lack of any impression or ring of ink or serrated edge which are characteristic of letterpress and gravure.

PRINCIPLE OF OFFSET LITHOGRAPHY

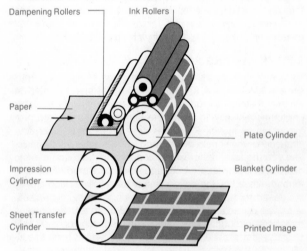

Like letterpress, offset lithography has equipment for short, medium and long runs. Both sheet-fed and web presses are used. Sheet-fed lithography is used for printing advertising, books, catalogs, greeting cards, posters, labels, packaging, folding boxes, decalcomanias, coupons, trading stamps, and art reproduction. Also many sheet-fed presses can *perfect* (print both sides of the paper) in one pass through the press. Web offset is used for printing business forms, newspapers, pre-printed newspaper inserts, advertising literature, catalogs, books, encyclopedias, and magazines. Web presses are gradually replacing sheet-fed.

## Collotype—Screenless Printing

Collotype or photogelatin printing reproduces illustrations in continuous tone or without halftone dots. Until recently, it was the only screenless printing process. Screenless printing can also be done by lithography.

Collotype is a reproduction process which uses bichromated gelatin as a printing medium and is capable of high quality reproduction in runs from 100 to 5,000. Platemaking and printing are extremely critical compared with the other printing processes. It is used for posters and transparencies printed on both sides for back-lighted displays. Collotype is also used for fine art reproductions, mounted displays and counter cards.

In screenless printing by lithography, continuous-tone films, usually positives, are used on special plates with long scale of tone reproduction. Platemaking is critical. The main advantages of screenless printing are high resolution, no screen moiré and greater purity of color especially in tints and middle tones.

## SCREEN PRINTING

Formerly known as silk screen, this method employs a *porous* screen of fine silk, Nylon, Dacron, or stainless steel mounted on a frame. A stencil is produced on the screen, either manually or photomechanically, in which the non-printing areas are protected by the stencil. Printing is done on paper or other substrate under the screen by applying ink with a paint-like consistency to the screen, spreading and forcing it through the fine mesh openings with a rubber squeegee. The production rate, formerly limited by the drying time of the ink, has been greatly increased through the development of automatic presses, improved dryers and UV inks. Recently, rotary screen presses have been introduced which speed up production considerably because they allow continuous operation. Screen printing usually can be recognized by the thick layer of ink and sometimes by the texture of the screen on the printing.

PRINCIPLE OF SCREEN PRINTING

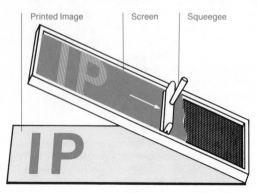

Printed Image    Screen    Squeegee

Versatility is the principal advantage of screen printing. Any surface can be printed—wood, glass, metal, plastic, fabric, cork, etc.—in any shape or design, any thickness, and in any size. In advertising, screen printing is used for banners, decals, posters, 24-sheet billboards, car cards, counter displays, menu covers, etc. Heavy paperboards can be printed, eliminating costly mounting. Wallpapers and draperies are printed because of the depth of colors afforded—especially in the short-run custom designs of interior decorators. There are many other specialty uses for screen printing, such as decorating melamine plastic sheets before lamination and the printing of electronic circuit boards.

## ELECTRONIC AND JET PRINTING

Electronic and jet printing are pressureless and plateless printing processes like Xerox 9700 and A.B. Dick Videojet that use computers, electronics, electrostatics, and special toners and inks to compose and produce images. They are more adaptable to the printing of variable information as in addressing, coding, billing forms, computer letters, etc., but they can be used for short run publishing. These processes are described in more detail on page 139.

## COPYING AND DUPLICATING—REPROGRAPHY

Copying and duplicating are also called *Reprography.* For less than 10 copies, the copier offers the fastest, most convenient and economical method of duplication. Above 10 copies, high-speed copiers and/or duplicators are used. Reprography is used extensively by in-house printing departments and quick printing shops. There are now about 80,000 such installations in the U.S.

Before 1940 the only method for making copies of documents was the *Photostat* which was cumbersome, time-consuming and expensive. Since then, a number of photocopying systems were developed. Among the first were the diffusion transfer processes by Gevaert and Agfa in Europe. 3M soon followed with Thermography (copying with heat—not to be confused with the printing process on page 26). These processes flourished until Xerox introduced the 914 Copier in 1960. Since then electrophotography has dominated the copier market.

**Electrophotography** is based on electrostatic transfer of toner to and from a charged photoconductor surface. There are plain paper and special coated paper copiers. Both types use electrophotographic coatings such as selenium, cadmium sulfide, zinc oxide, or organic photoconductors to produce the images in the copier. These materials have the unique property of holding an electrostatic charge in the dark, and losing the charge when exposed to light such as that reflected from the white areas of an original. The image areas which remain charged are developed with an oppositely charged dry powder or liquid toner and are fixed by heat, pressure or solvent vapor. In some copiers the toner is transferred from the electrophotographic surface onto plain paper using electrostatic attraction. In the case of the transfer process, the electrophotographic coating is cleaned and can be re-imaged many times.

Copiers can have many special features such as push-button operation for enlargement or reduction, color copying, two side copying, automatic copy feed, copy counting, collating, and even imaging from microfilm. New sophisticated copiers like Xerox 9500 and Kodak Ektaprint 250 are complete publishing systems with binding and finishing, and compete with copier/duplicators in runs up to 300.

### Offset Duplicator

When copies in quantities up to 10,000 are needed, the most economical printing method is the *offset duplicator,* which is a small offset press as is described on page 140.

**The Copier/Duplicator** automates duplicating by combining a *copier* and a *duplicator.* In the system an electrophotographic copier makes the plate, a transport device automatically mounts the plate on the duplicator and treats it with a chemical to convert it to a printing plate; the press prints the number of copies programmed into the counter, rejects the old plate, and either turns itself off or inserts a new plate and continues to print.

### Stencil and Spirit Duplicators

These two less expensive and less sophisticated systems for duplicating have been in use for many years. The *stencil duplicator,* or mimeograph, which works by forcing ink through a stencil usually prepared on a typewriter, or by spark discharge, produces copies of acceptable quality on plain paper.

The *spirit duplicator* is unique in that the master can be made to print more than one color at the same time using special carbon papers which contain soluble dyed resins of different colors. A special printing paper is wet with a fast-drying solvent which, when brought in contact with the spirit master, softens and tackifies the resin so that a small amount of coloring dye is transferred to the paper. The master can be printed, and re-printed, until all the dye in the ink is used up, which is usually about 100 prints.

# Type and typographic imaging

Printing can be defined as the reproduction in quantity of words and pictures on a page. In the photo-mechanical processes such as offset, any original camera-ready material to be printed is referred to as *copy* by the printer. Copy consists of all material to be reproduced in text or picture form. The term can be confusing however because the word ''copy'' is also used to refer to *manuscript copy*, which is the author's manuscript to be set in type. This section will deal with text copy, or type, and describe the various methods of typesetting.

## TYPE FUNDAMENTALS

Type faces are usually available in 6 to 72 point, with a complete *font* in each size. A font is defined as a complete assortment of any one size and style of type containing all the characters for setting ordinary composition.

Capital letters are called *upper case* and small letters, *lower case*. When old-time compositors set type by hand, they placed the case with the capital letters above the case with the small letters, thus the nomenclature.

In lower case letters the upper stroke (as in the letter ''b'') is called the *ascender,* and the downward stroke (as in ''p'') is known as the *descender.* The short crossline at the end of the main strokes is called the *serif.* Type faces without serifs are called *sans serif.* The *body* or *x-height* makes up the greatest portion of a letter.

Type size cannot be measured from the top of an ascending letter to the bottom of a descending letter. The face of any letter is not the full point size. For example, the face of a 36-pt. letter may measure only 30 points.

Corresponding letters in the same size type may vary in height. We say that the face is either small on body (small x-height) or large on body (large x-height). For example, the following are all 24-pt. lower case ''h'':

h **h** h **h** h **h** h **h** h **h** h

To most people, many type faces look alike; even an expert must look carefully to differentiate between them. While there is no short cut in learning how to identify type faces, careful study

HELVETICA MEDIUM IN 11 DIFFERENT SIZES

6  ABCDEFGHIJKLMNOPQRSTUVWXYZABCDEFG
8  ABCDEFGHIJKLMNOPQRSTUVWXYZ
10  ABCDEFGHIJKLMNOPQRSTU
12  ABCDEFGHIJKLMNOPQR
14  ABCDEFGHIJKLMNOP
18  ABCDEFGHIJKLM
24  ABCDEFGHI
30  ABCDEFG
42  ABCDE
48  ABCD
60  ABC

of a few key letters helps. For example, the lower case "g" is one of the most distinctive letters. The elements are: the top loop, the lower loop, the hook off the top loop, and the element joining the two loops. By studying the size, shape and position of these elements, the type face identity can be more easily determined. Other distinctive letters are "p" "a" "e" and "t".

The entire appearance of a printed piece can be affected by the selection of type faces. Many characteristics—masculinity, femininity, delicacy, formality, etc.—can be suggested by the type face used. The guidance of a qualified designer, printer or typographer in selecting the proper type face is indispensable.

Above all, remember type was designed to be read easily! Both the selection of the type face and the size to be used must be considered. Use italics with care! Their primary purpose is for emphasis, not to be read in a mass.

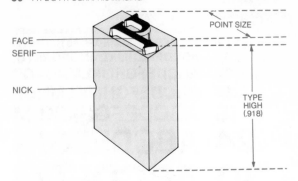

## CLASSIFICATION OF TYPE FACES

There are many approaches to type classification, none of which are precise. The following, however, is a useful break-down covering a wide variety of type faces:

**Oldstyle** This type style group, patterned after letter forms used on classical Roman inscriptions, looks better in mass than when examined letter by letter. The letters have high readability because they are open, wide and round, with pointed serifs that make a pleasing contrast between the heavy and light strokes. Garamond and Caslon are examples.

**Modern** The term *modern* refers not to a time period, but to a style of type designed almost 200 years ago. These types have a much greater degree of mechanical perfection than Oldstyle faces and are distinguished by extreme contrast between thick and thin strokes, with thin squared off serifs. Times Roman, Bodoni and Didot are examples.

**Square Serif** A contemporary type style used mainly for display, headlines, and small amounts of reading matter. The letters have square or blocked serifs and more or less uniform strokes, and the face is even in texture and weight with very little contrast. Clarendon, Stymie and Cairo are examples.

**Sans Serif** This type enjoys great popularity because of its simplicity of design. The letters have no serifs, and the face is generally even in overall weight with very little contrast between thick and thin strokes. Helvetica, News Gothic and Futura are examples. (The *Pocket Pal* is set in Helvetica.)

**Script** Designed to simulate handwriting, script type is used mostly for special effects, formal invitations, and announcements. There are no serifs or extreme contrast between the

ABCDEFGHIJKLMNOPQRSTUVW
abcdefghijklmnopqrstuvwxyzabcdefghij
OLD STYLE                                                    GARAMOND

ABCDEFGHIJKLMNOPQRSTUV
abcdefghijklmnopqrstuvwxyzabcdefg
MODERN                                                    TIMES ROMAN

ABCDEFGHIJKLMNOPQRST
abcdefghijklmnopqrstuvwxyza
SQUARE SERIF                                                   CLARENDON

ABCDEFGHIJKLMNOPQRSTUVWX
abcdefghijklmnopqrstuvwxyzabcde
SANS SERIF                                                   HELVETICA

*ABCDEFGHIJKLMNOPQRS*
*abcdefghijklmnopqrstuvwxyzabcdefg*
SCRIPT                                              COMMERCIAL SCRIPT

𝕬𝕭𝕮𝕯𝕰𝕱𝕲𝕳𝕴𝕵𝕶𝕷𝕸𝕹𝕺𝕻𝕼𝕽𝕾𝕿𝖀
abcdefghijklmnopqrstuvwxyzabcdefg
TEXT LETTERS                                              OLD ENGLISH

**ABCDEFGHIJKLMNOPQR**
**abcdefghijklmnopqrstuvw**
DECORATIVE                                                    COMSTOCK

thick and thin strokes, and the letters seem to touch each other.
Commercial Script and Bank Script are examples.

**Text Letters** This group resembles the hand-drawn letters of
the early scribes. It is usually selected for religious documents,
certificates, diplomas and invitations, and is rarely used otherwise. Old English and Engravers Text are examples.

**Decorative Types** These are novelty styles or faces and used
primarily to command attention. They are generally contemporary faces and do not fit any of the standard classifications.
Designed to express different moods, they may be eccentric in
appearance. Comstock is one example.

## Type Families

Some types have many variations, and these various styles are said to be in the same family. Examples of these variations in a type style are: *light face, medium, bold, extra bold, expanded,* and *condensed,* with italic versions of each in most cases.

A FAMILY OF TYPE

Helvetica Light
*Helvetica Light Italic*
Helvetica Regular
*Helvetica Regular Italic*
**Helvetica Medium**
***Helvetica Medium Italic***
**Helvetica Bold**
***Helvetica Bold Italic***
Helvetica Regular Condensed
*Helvetica Regular Condensed Italic*

### READABILITY AND LEGIBILITY

Most people who are not concerned with the fine points of typography use readability and legibility synonymously. But there is a distinct difference: readability is the ease of reading a printed page, whereas legibility refers to the speed with which each letter or word can be recognized. Readability refers to the type arrangement; legibility is concerned with type design.

Readability and legibility are dependent upon several factors that must be considered when selecting a type face. These include texture and finish of paper, color of ink, type face, size of type, line length, line spacing, etc. Type should be set to be read with little effort or eyestrain. Proper line spacing is important to the appearance of an ad or a printed piece. Each job presents a different problem, depending on the type style used, whether capital letters or lower case letters are to be used, etc. Good type designers will give that little extra service, in the best interests of their customers, to be sure that the spacing enhances the typography. In practice, good spacing is often a matter of common sense.

NO LETTERSPACING

# LETTERSPACING IS THE AMOUNT OF

2 POINT LETTERSPACING

# LETTERSPACING IS THE AM

4 POINT LETTERSPACING

# LETTERSPACING IS THE

**Letterspacing** is the amount of space between letters, negative or positive, either for readability, aesthetics or to fill a certain area. It is used mostly in capital letters for display with small amounts of positive letterspace, or in "tight" typography or *kerning*, with negative letterspace. Some lines require corrective letterspacing to make all letters appear optically evenly spaced.

**Negative letterspacing** involves the removal of space between letters individually (kerning), or between all letters equally (called "white space reduction").

**Line spacing** The amount of space between lines is known as leading and is always expressed in points or fractions of a point. There is no set rule to follow. Too much leading can sometimes be as bad as not enough. Type faces with long ascenders and descenders require more leading. Also, the wider the measure of text composition, the more leading is required for good readability. In photographic typesetting, leading refers to the vertical movement of the photo material, forward or reverse, and is usually measured from baseline to baseline.

NO LINE SPACING

The amount of space between lines is known as leading. There is no set rule to follow. Too much leading can sometimes be as bad as not enough. Type faces with

1 POINT LINE SPACING

The amount of space between lines is known as leading. There is no set rule to follow. Too much leading can sometimes be as bad as not enough. Type faces with

2 POINT LINE SPACING

The amount of space between lines is known as leading. There is no set rule to follow. Too much leading can sometimes be as bad as not enough. Type faces with

## PRINTERS' MEASUREMENTS

The *point* and the *pica* are two units of measure universally used in printing in most English-speaking countries. Their use is primarily in typesetting. Type size is measured in points. Line length measure is in picas and points. The pica is used to express overall width or depth as well as the length of a line.

**The point** measures .0138 or approximately 1/72 of an inch. In other words, there are 72 points to the inch. All type is designated in points (10-point Caslon, 24-point Baskerville, etc.). Points are always used to specify the *size* of type. Type faces may be set in sizes from 4 to 144 points, but are generally used in 6 to 72 points. Line spacing is also specified in points (2 points of leading, etc.).

**The pica** is used for *linear* measurements of type. (A pica gauge is the printer's measuring tool.) There are 12 points to 1 pica, or 6 picas to 1 inch. The length of a line is specified in picas, as well as the depth of a type area. For example, a given block of copy is to be set 20 picas wide by 36 picas deep. Inches are never used in type measurement.

**The em** is also important in typesetting although not a part of the point system. It is the square of the type size (a 10-pt. em is 10 points wide and 10 points high) and is used for measuring the *quantity* of type. The most common use of the em space today is that of paragraph indention. An *en* space is one half of an *em;* a *thin* is either ¼ or ⅓ of an *em* space. These *fixed spaces* are used for tabular composition.

**The agate line** is a measurement used by newspapers to sell advertising space. There are 14 agate lines to an inch. An agate line refers to the space occupied by one line of agate type in one column. The width of the column can vary from paper to paper. A 60 line ad can take several forms: 60 agate lines in one column; 30 agate lines in 2 columns, etc.

## PROOFREADERS' MARKS

The proofreaders' marks shown on the following pages are standard and should be familiar to everyone working with type. It is important to use these accepted signs, rather than others which will not be understood by the typesetter. Marking changes with a colored pen or pencil enables the typesetter to see the corrections more easily. The illustration on page 43 shows how these symbols are used in actual practice.

### Delete and Insert

| | |
|---|---|
| *ℓ* | Delete, take out! |
| *ℓ̄* | Delete and closeup |
| *l/s* | LETTER SP A CE |
| # | Insert space(more space) |
| ☐ | Em quad space or indention |
| *stet* | Let it stand—(all matter above dots) |

### Punctuation Marks

| | |
|---|---|
| ⊙ | Period |
| ⋏ | Comma |
| ; | Semicolon |
| : | Colon |
| ᴠ | Apostrophe or 'single quote' |
| ⁶⁶ | Open quotes |
| ⁹⁹ | Close quotes |
| ?/ | Question mark |
| !/ | Exclamation point |
| = | Hyphen |
| (/) | Parentheses |
| /—/ | Dash |

### Style of Type

| | |
|---|---|
| *wf* | Wrong **style of type** |
| *lc* | Set in LOWER CASE or LOWER CASE |
| *caps* | SET IN capital letters |
| *caps+lc* | Lower case with Initial Caps |
| *sc* | SET IN small capitals |
| *rom* | Set in *roman* type |
| *ital* | Set in italic type |

*lf*    Set in (**light face**) type

*bf*    **Set in** bold face **type**

### Spacing

⌒    Close up entirely; take out space

⌣    Less ⌣ space ⌣ between ⌣ words

\#    Insert space

### Paragraphing and Position

⌐    Move to right ⌐

⌐    ⌐ Move to left

⊔    Lower (letters or words)

⊓    Raise (letters or words)

=    Align horizontally

‖    Align vertically

¶    Begin a paragraph

*no* ¶    No paragraph.

*run in*    Run in

*flush* ¶    No paragraph indention

*tr*    Transpose letters in a word

*tr*    Transpose enclosed in circle (matter)

### Miscellaneous

✕    Broken type

⊙    Invert (upside-down type)

↓    Push down space

(sp)    Spell out (Capt.) Smith)

*ok* ᵂ/c    OK "with corrections"

*ok* ᵃ/c    or "as corrected"

(···)    Ellipsis

**Proof with Errors Marked**

*cap*  THE PRACTICE OF TYPOGRAPHY, if it be followed  *tr*

faithfully, is hard work—full of detail, full petty  *of*

restrictions full of drudgery, and not Greatly  *lc*

rewørded as men now count rewards: There are  ⊙

times when we need to bring to it, all the history

and art and feeling that w can, to make it beara-  *e*

ble.

*no* ¶  But in the light of history and of art, and of  ⋀

knowledge and of mans achievement, it is as

interesting a work as exists—a broad and

# humanizingemployment which can *indeed* be  *rom*

*eq* #  followed merely as a trade, but which if per-

*wf*  fected into an art, or even broadened into a pro-  ⌞⌟

fession, will perpetually open new horizons to

*tr*  eyes our and opportunities to our hands.

—D. B. Updike  *sc*

**Proof after Corrections Have Been Made**

THE PRACTICE OF TYPOGRAPHY, if it be followed
faithfully, is hard work—full of detail, full of petty restrictions, full of drudgery, and not greatly
rewarded as men now count rewards. There are
times when we need to bring to it all the history
and art and feeling that we can, to make it
bearable. But in the light of history, and of art,
and of knowledge and of man's achievement, it is
as interesting a work as exists—a broad and
humanizing employment which can indeed be
followed merely as a trade, but which if perfected
into an art, or even broadened into a profession,
will perpetually open new horizons to our eyes
and opportunities to our hands.    —D. B. UPDIKE

## TYPESETTING

After the different characteristics and styles of type are known, it is important to be familiar with the various methods of typesetting. There are three basic methods of producing type: cast metal or hot type composition, typewriter or strike-on composition (sometimes called "cold type"), and photographic typesetting. Hot type refers to cast metal type whether it is set by hand or machine. Continuing development has widened the choice of typesetting methods, especially in phototypesetting.

### Hand Composition

Hand-set composition is produced with individual metal characters assembled into lines much as Gutenberg did in 1450. A *composing stick* is held in one hand while the letters are selected from a type case with the other and placed in the stick until a full line is set. Different size spaces are then inserted between words to *justify* the line, filling it out to the desired width (called "justification"). This is repeated until all the copy has been set. For line spacing, or when an exact depth is wanted for a block of type, metal strips or slugs (called "leads," pronounced *ledds)* are inserted between the lines. The process of returning the type to the case is called *distribution*.

### Machine Composition

Machine-set copy can be produced on any of four machines. The Linotype and Intertype machines cast a line of type at a time; the Monotype system produces individual characters; and the Ludlow machine, which also casts one line of type at a time.

**Linotype, Intertype** machines cast a one-piece line of metal type. At the touch of a key, a *matrix* (a mold for each character) is released from a *magazine* (storage case). Once all the matrices (characters) for one line are assembled, the line is automatically justified by special *spacebands* (or wedges, which expand the space between words). The line is moved into the casting mechanism where molten metal is forced into the character molds. After the first line has been cast and the slug ejected from the mold, the matrices are returned to the magazine, ready to be used again. Each size of each type face has its own magazine.

Some linecasting machines have been equipped for semi-automatic operation from perforated tape. The tape can be prepared on tape perforators or received over telephone lines. With tape-controlled linecasting, the machine output is greatly increased. Maximum speed depends on the machine, and it takes several keyboard operators to keep one tape-controlled machine busy.

LINECASTING MACHINE

Caster | Keyboard | Magazine

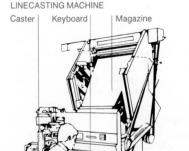

**Monotype** is a combination of two machines: a *keyboard* (per-forator), and a *typecaster,* which casts the characters one by one rather than as a complete line. As the operator types the copy, a perforated paper tape is produced which is used to drive the typecaster. To justify the lines of type, a counting mecha-nism automatically registers the widths of the characters as they are typed. When the maximum number of characters per line has been reached, a bell rings to alert the operator. A series of keys is struck to determine how much additional space must be added to justify the line. Up to this point we have only a perfo-rated, or coded paper roll. To set the type, the roll is fed into the typecaster, where it drives the casting mechanism by means of compressed air. One advantage of Monotype is that corrections can be made by hand, character by character, rather than re-casting a line.

**Ludlow** is a semi-automatic method of typesetting, combining hand and machine composition. Individual character matrices are assembled by hand in a special composing stick. The justi-fied line is then inserted into the Ludlow machine, and mechani-cally cast into a slug. While this operation is similar to hand composition, the advantage is that a new slug is made for each line of type. This gives the printer an unlimited supply of type from one set of matrices. Ludlow is especially suitable for dis-play type and headings.

## Assembly: Press Lockup

In metal composition methods, type is locked up in a *chase* (a heavy rectangular steel frame). Lockup is done on a large table called a *stone,* so named because originally it had a stone top; today the top is steel. The form does not take up the entire area inside the chase, and the empty spaces are filled up with *furniture* (wood or metal blocks). In addition to the furniture, *quoins* (steel wedge-shaped devices) are placed on two adjacent sides of the form between the furniture. The quoins are tightened slightly, and the form is planed for levelness. Once all the parts are level, the quoins are tightened to hold the form securely.

CHASE | Furniture | Type | Quoins

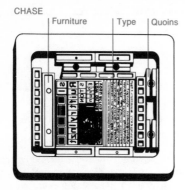

## IMAGE CONVERSION SYSTEMS

Image conversion systems are mechanical or photomechanical processes for converting metal type and engravings into photographic or other film for use in photomechanical platemaking processes. These systems are used to convert letterpress plates and type forms for offset lithography, gravure, and for letterpress wraparound and photopolymer plates. Relief image carriers are converted in two ways: (1) by pulling inked reproduction proofs, on special proof presses; and (2) by direct transfer of the image, either photographically, or by a combination of mechanical and chemical methods.

## TYPEWRITER OR STRIKE-ON COMPOSITION

This is usually referred to as *cold type,* although the term has little significance. Several machines are used in strike-on composition. These are the VariTyper, the Friden Justowriter, and IBM's Selectric Composer (SC) system. All have proportionally-designed type faces and produce justified composition.

**VariTyper** machines require double typing for justified composition, and can mix two fonts in the same line. After setting the carriage for a particular line length, the operator types the line until a signal indicates the line is within justification range. The operator tabs over and retypes the line at that time. The VariTyper word spacing mechanism automatically adds or subtracts space between words to permit justification.

The **Justowriter** system utilizes paper tape and two typing units. The recorder generates a perforated paper tape with line endings in justification range and a hard copy (typewritten) printout. The paper tape is then inserted into a reproducing unit. The tape is read and strike-on type produced automatically in a justified form.

IBM's stand-alone **Selectric Composer,** like the VariTyper, is a single-unit machine that requires double typing for justified composition. Because it carries a single "ball" font, it cannot set mixed composition in the same line without complicated ball-changing. The MT system is more sophisticated in operation and requires only a single typing. It consists of one or more recorders that produce unjustified copy and coded input magnetic tape. If the input is correct, the magnetic tape is processed, and a Selectric Composer sets justified composition. If there are corrections, these can be made on another magnetic tape, and the tape reader merges the correction tape with the original tape to produce the final composition. *(See Word Processing on page 59.)*

IBM MT SYSTEM

Recorder          Selectric Composer

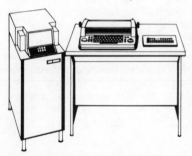

## PHOTOGRAPHIC TYPESETTING

Metal typesetting has gradually given way to phototypesetting and other direct-image composition. These reduce the number of production steps leading up to the complete page pasteup required in platemaking for every major printing process. Even letterpress is now using phototypesetting for photopolymer and other photomechanical plates.

Besides typewriter composition there are three types of direct-image processes:

(1) Phototypesetting of varying electronic sophistication, automation, imaging speed, and typographic versatility. Producing composition from simple straight matter to full-page, multi-column formats combining text and display, on photographic paper, film, or paper plates.

(2) Photolettering and Photo-display. This category covers equipment specifically oriented to the production of headline typesetting. The Filmtype, PhotoTypositor, and Staromat are examples.

(3) Transfer lettering and *paper type*. This category includes manually manipulated materials used in simple character-by-character composition of words and lines for heads and display where production speed is not a factor.

These processes have a place in the new technology of composition. It is not unusual to find sophisticated phototypesetters together with hand-operated display equipment in the same composing room or printing department. In this case, perhaps the manual devices are used only for occasional display settings or for little-used type faces.

## How Photographic Typesetting Works

All photographic typesetting requires three elements: a master character image, a light source, and a photo- or light-sensitive material. Phototypesetting systems have undergone three major evolutionary changes from the development of the first phototypesetting device.

**First generation** These units are adaptations of machine-set typesetting. The Fotosetter (introduced in 1950) was essentially an Intertype linecaster. The Monophoto was essentially a Monotype. In these machines the master character image was carried on the matrix. The matrix contained a film negative of the character and was photographed instead of cast. First generation phototypesetters were mechanical in nature and used slower tungsten light sources.

**Second generation** These units are electro-mechanical in nature. The Photon 200B (introduced in 1954) was the first working device utilizing new technology. Today there are well over 100 models available from many manufacturers. Here is a diagram of a typical phototypesetter of this type.

| Photo Paper or Film | Positioning Element | Turret Lens | Font Disc | Light Source |

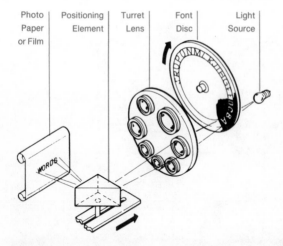

**Third generation** These units utilize cathode-ray-tube or laser technology and are totally electronic. Characters are usually formed by a series of minute dots or lines. The resultant image is then transferred to photographic material. Because third generation typesetters set type with a beam of light they are capable of extremely high speeds (over 1,000 30-character 8-point lines in a minute). This is also called *digitized* typesetting to better describe the method of forming characters.

Although devices have been introduced that claim to be fourth and fifth generation, there has been no technological breakthrough that combines the quality, speed, graphics handling and non-chemical orientation that would characterize such a device. *(See Other Imaging Systems page 52.)*

### Character Storage

All phototypesetters must store their master character sets in some form. These sets include all of the characters and symbols for a particular type style. Some of these photomatrices may contain as few as one or as many as eighteen fonts. On some, the master character image is enlarged by individual lenses or by a zoom lens. On others the size on the matrix determines the type size. The width values for each character of every font on the photomatrix must be stored so that the photo output unit can properly space characters. Photomatrices may be plastic or glass or film and are configured as disks, grids, strips, drums, segments, and quadrants *(see illustration next page)*.

TYPE FONT CONFIGURATIONS

Disc

Grid

Drum

Film Strip/Segment

## Photographic Imaging

Copy to be typeset is usually input to a phototypesetter by tape, paper or magnetic, or floppy magnetic disc (although direct input by keyboard is also utilized). Characters are then selected by referencing certain marks on the photomatrix which refer to certain characters. When the proper mark is reached a burst of light from a xenon flash lamp is exposed through the master character image. This beam of light is then deflected to the correct optical path by mirrors or prisms, enlarged by lenses and then positioned on photosensitive output material.

## Optical Systems

Phototypesetters differ in their basic approach to imaging. Some use lenses (one for each size enlargement) that are mounted in a turret. Some use a zoom lens that telescopes to the particular enlargement size. Characters may be positioned by prisms, mirrors, lenses and fiber optic bundles that move on a track, or mirrors that rotate.

## Imaging Speed

Phototypesetting speed is usually measured in newspaper lines per minute (lpm). A standard line is 8 point, 11 picas with 30 characters. Most second generation phototypesetters average 50 lpm with a high of 150 lpm. The speed of direct input machines, like hot-metal linecasters, is determined by the speed of the operator. You can determine *characters per second* by dividing *lines per minute* in half.

## CRT Typesetters

Third generation phototypesetters are capable of greatly increased speeds and can also, in some cases, create complete pages of text, headline and graphics material *in position*. Characters are stored as either master images or as digitized information and then translated into dot placement.

In operation, as copy and typographic commands on paper tape or magnetic tape are read and analyzed, patterns of the needed characters are called out of the memory section and are imaged in correct size at their precise positions on the page or format. It is this finished composition that is exposed to the photopaper, film, or offset plate being used.

Though character images are solid and accurately contoured shapes after imaging and printing, they are actually patterns of characters, and consist of adjoining sweeps of scan lines, similar to the buildup of images on television screens. The density of these scan lines to the inch determines the typographic quality of the imaged characters and the imaging speed of any particular digitized system. The more scan lines to the inch, the higher the resolution (sharpness) of the characters. The less scan lines to the inch, such as in a proof mode, the lower the resolution and the faster the output. Characters may be electronically obliqued, backslanted, condensed, expanded or reversed.

Shown here is a simplified, enlarged and outlined diagram of one system's pattern buildup of a 9-point character. Imagine that each outlined bar is a solid black bar or line. It takes 62 of these scan lines in less than $\frac{1}{16}''$ to image this 9-point character. In this outlined diagram, the solid scan lines merge optically to form a smoothly contoured character that is as sharp to the eyes as a similar character imaged in a single flash inside a regular phototypesetter or printed from the face of metal type. To simulate the optical merging of scan lines, hold this page at arm's length and squint your eyes as you look at the pattern of the "B".

## Other Imaging Systems

Printout devices for data and word processing have traditionally been *impact* oriented, striking a ribbon to create characters on plain paper. *Dot matrix* approaches form the character as a set of dots, positioned within a pre-arranged grid:

5×7 GRID                    5×7 LETTER "N"

*Non-Impact* printers produce characters with smaller dots and at higher speeds through a variety of methods. *Inkjet* devices "squirt" minute droplets of ink through a single or multiple nozzles. *Electro erosion* devices remove a coating of aluminum from black paper. *Electro photographic* devices use lasers or electronics to change the electrical charge on zinc oxide coated paper and then attract particles of black toner. The image may also be created on a charged drum or other surface and then transferred onto paper, as in *Xerography.*

The application of these technologies has blurred the definition of certain devices. Copiers traditionally reproduced an existing image. Printers created images from a pre-stored set in their memory. High speed copiers were called *duplicators.* The use of lasers to create images (as a printer would) on copier/duplicators has created new reprographic tools capable of combining the functions of typewriter or printer and copier or duplicator.

Printers that produce graphics, charts and schematics are called *plotters.* They can also print out rudimentary color and coarse illustrations. Present trends indicate that the functional capabilities of all printer and copier devices are merging.

Combined with *digitizing scanners,* which reduce images to dots stored in memory, these printer/copiers can also print out line art, logos and coarse photographs as well as text, set in reduced typographic quality levels. The coarse dot matrix has evolved into the *pixel* (or *pel*) which stands for "picture element"—a minute dot that can be positioned to create images.

Pixels are stored in system memory, coded to each individual *printout* position (called a *bit map*), and output via the applicable imaging technique. Although pixel levels are about 300 to the inch, it is expected that they will increase to 600 or more. Graphic arts quality levels begin at approximately 900 pixels (or dots to the inch).

Thus, new technologies will challenge the traditional typesetting machine, incorporating advanced imaging techniques, directed at business communication but eventually affecting the printing and publishing industries.

## Input

All phototypesetting devices must have some form of input. The major forms of input are:

**Direct input** Here the typesetting device is connected to a keyboard. Thus the speed of the typesetter is directly related to the input speed of the operator. Some machines let the operator record all input for later playback on a floppy disk.

**Off-line keyboard** This type of device produces a "record" of the information keyed, in the form of perforated paper tape or magnetic medium. In some cases, the operator may make the hyphenation and justification decisions. The keyboard is then called *counting* and the input *justified.* When no decisions are made by the input operator because the computer will hyphenate and justify, the keyboard is called *non-counting* and the input, unjustified or *idiot.*

**Optical character recognition (OCR)** technology has the ability to take typewritten sheets and scan them to produce a recorded medium. The OCR machine *reads* the typed images and then determines each character. Thus anyone who produces manuscript copy can provide pages directly for input and thus avoid redundant rekeyboarding. Newer *omnifont* scanners can read any typewriter or printed characters.

**Video display terminals (VDT)** These units also use CRTs. However, a VDT screen is used to show words (instead of pictures), and thus allows an operator to view the contents of input tape or stored information, and then to add, delete or change copy at will. VDTs may be *standalone,* with their own media, or *systems terminals,* connected to computer systems.

Designed originally as an editing device, rapid changes in technology have made the VDT one of the more useful tools in today's phototypesetting department. Operators may now not only edit pre-keyboarded copy, but also do area makeup directly on the screen. Some VDTs allow tabular material to be shown on the screen exactly as it will be typeset, line for line, thus allowing the operator to check lineup and fit before actual typesetting. A few large newspapers are using VDTs in conjunction with mass storage devices as direct connection to typesetters. Reporters and feature writers keyboard their articles directly into a VDT where they may see their article as it will appear in type. This material is then stored on magnetic discs or tapes. Editors then call out this information on master VDTs, edit, format and send it directly to on-line typesetters, thus eliminating rekeyboarding. At present there are more than 100 manufacturers of VDTs.

VDT EDITING TERMINAL

**Electronic Editing**

The video screen has become the pervasive tool of modern text and graphics technology. It is the most visible part of word processing, personal computers, all levels of typesetting equipment—and data processing, of course. Although there are differences in technique, most video approaches are similar.

All activity on the screen takes place at the position indicated by the *cursor*, a blip of light that can be moved. Cursor control keys usually have arrows for the up, down, left and right movement. Additionally, a *home* key returns the cursor to the upper lefthand corner of the screen.

The data displayed on the screen represents a part of the *file* that is stored in memory. To see a section of the memory data on the screen, a technique called *scrolling* is used to move the memory data up and down to bring the required section onto the screen. In effect, scrolling is like winding and unwinding a scroll.

An alternate approach to scrolling is the *next screen* technique which allows the operator to bring the next *screenful* of data to the screen in one block.

At the cursor position, the operator may add, delete or change a character. Addition or deletion are part of an automated function that opens or closes the working area. Deleted characters appear to vanish as all characters on the right move one character position to the left to close up the hole from the deleted

SCROLLING

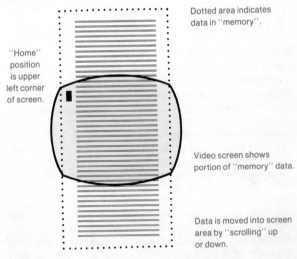

Dotted area indicates data in "memory".

"Home" position is upper left corner of screen.

Video screen shows portion of "memory" data.

Data is moved into screen area by "scrolling" up or down.

character. In addition, the reverse occurs as each character moves to the right to make room for the new character. A change is usually a substitution of one character for another.

Words that do not fit on a line are automatically moved to the next line. This is called "full word wraparound" or "word wrap". Word spaces may be either blank or a symbol may be used to indicate their presence.

A "block define" function allows the operator to indicate the beginning and end of a certain section of copy. The cursor is positioned at the first character of the section and a key or keys are pressed that indicate "begin block". The opposite is done at the end. The operator can now delete the block in its entirety or move it. The cursor is positioned at the point where the block is to begin and a key or keys are depressed that indicate "move block". This function is then performed immediately.

Functions that are performed on the screen within moments of the operator's request are called *foreground* functions. Functions that must take place off-screen are called *background* functions. Electronic editing is always a foreground approach.

To see the files that are stored on the system's magnetic memory the operator requests a "screen directory". This shows the names of the files in memory with additional information, such as the number of characters that are stored. The operator can request a file by calling for it by name and it then appears on the screen with the beginning of the file at the cursor's home position. The operator can also file the material back to memory which records it on the magnetic floppy or rigid disk.

*File Management* is the storage and retrieval of information.

### Multi-Terminal Systems (Front Ends)

It was inevitable that all of the pieces of the typesetting and composition process would be linked together into a cohesive *system*. Initially, a number of VDTs were connected to a central computer to share its processing power. This approach is called a *cluster*. Because of the volume of information that passed through this cluster system, a memory storage element had to be added. The first of these was magnetic tape, but it was *serial* in nature and slowed down the ability to reach any particular piece of information.

Next came *random access*, which refers to disk recording. Disks are like phonograph records—a read/write head can move to any location on the disk more rapidly than searching through magnetic tape. There are two types of disks: *Floppy* disks are flexible mylar coated with a metallic oxide and can store 250,000 to 600,000 characters on 5″ *mini floppy* versions or 300,000 to 1,000,000 characters on standard 8″ floppies. Floppy disks can be either single or dual sided. *Rigid* (or hard) disks can store from one million to several million characters and can rotate faster, thus permitting faster *access* time. The term *megabyte* refers to each million characters of storage. Rigid disks are either *fixed* or *removable*.

A TYPICAL FRONT END SYSTEM CONFIGURATION

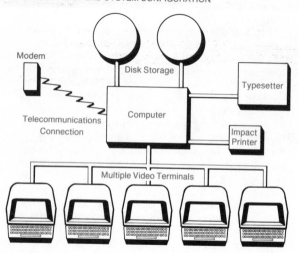

Modem

Disk Storage

Typesetter

Telecommunications Connection

Computer

Impact Printer

Multiple Video Terminals

The addition of memory modules required the cluster systems to develop approaches to storing and retrieving information. This is called *data* (or *file) management.* Jobs can be referenced by name or number, and the system will store them, later retrieving them by the name or number requested.

With the addition of memory management, the cluster systems were able to incorporate more sophisticated *programs* (or *software)* for typesetting and composition. These programs performed hyphenation and justification, pagination and other functions. And thus *computer typesetting, multi-terminal, data management* systems were born. Since it was the "front end" of the typesetting process, the term is often used.

As computerized phototypesetting can only act in response to input and input commands, it is the responsibility of the markup specialist to review manuscript copy and to add the computer codes that will be needed to do the typographic job at hand. Markup is called the *programming of typography.*

## Typesetting Commands

All typesetting input consists of two kinds of information: the *characters* you will see upon output, and the *commands* that determine how you will see them. Commands include changes in point size, type face, line length, leading (line spacing), positioning, tabular, columnar makeup, indention and others.

Commands may be preceded by a single code. This is called a *fixed field* approach, since the letters and numbers must be exactly right (for instance point size would need two digits, thus 9 point would have to be 09, etc.). Variable field commands have a beginning and ending code, thus allowing more variation in the data within.

Commands can be almost unintelligible if the letters used are not memory oriented *(mnemonic).* Too often, the programmer tried to stay with single letters, and then ran out. Newer systems start with multiple letters and are more human oriented.

TYPICAL COMMANDS

| | |
|---|---|
| *il | Indent Left |
| *ir | Indent Right |
| *ib | Indent Both (sides) |
| *rr | Ragged Right |
| *rl | Ragged Left |
| *cp | Change Point (size) |
| *cc | Change Column (measure) |
| *cf | Change Font |
| *cl | Change Leading |
| *ts | Tab Set |
| *ep | End Paragraph |

The present approach to commands for typesetting is called *generic coding*. Typed information is identified as *[text]* or *[head]* and then translated into the appropriate typographic parameters. Thus, authors and other editorial originators can code data by its generic appearance without regard to specific typographic specifications.

## Photographic Materials

Most phototypesetters expose photographic paper, film or an offset paper plate. Most users expose photo paper, either stabilization or true photomechanical. An inexpensive processor with two chemicals (activator and stabilizer) is used with stabilization paper. Tray development or more sophisticated processors are required for photomechanical or plate materials. Some typesetters are using a form of *dry silver* which permits processing by heat instead of chemistry.

## Typesetting Trends

Two trends have characterized modern typesetting development. The first is full page makeup (including halftones and drawings), and the second is dry output (no chemical processing). Lasers may play an important role in both areas. (The Associated Press LaserPhoto which is used to transmit halftones over telephone lines is indicative of the technology needed to create complete pages.) These trends are moving the typesetting process closer to platemaking in the graphic arts and copying in the office environment.

## Pagination

Typesetting is part of a larger process called composition. Type, art, illustrations, etc., are assembled into the final page format for pre-press requirements. Assembly is usually a manual operation, requiring pasteup (keylining) of page elements.

Most sophisticated photographic typesetters can position type so as to reduce the amount of page assembly. Heads and text can be output according to their page orientation. To accomplish this, commands must be given to the typesetter in coded form that translate the positioning information into machine instructions. A command for a two column page might sound like this: *set 30 lines from the start of the job, stop, back the photo material up to the start, indent over to the right the width of the first column plus a gutter space, set another 30 lines, stop, add extra space, repeat the operation.* Sophisticated software in front end systems automatically position all copy and produce fully paginated units according to pre-determined instructions in a *menu* of format alternatives.

**CAM** stands for Composition And Makeup (or Computer Assisted Makeup). It refers to video devices that show actual or simulated point size, type face, line length, leading, etc. They can be passive or interactive.

Passive CAMs are sometimes called "soft typesetters" or "previewers" since they only show how the typesetter will set the information in response to the commands.

Active or interactive CAMs let the operator change typographic format on the screen and instantly see what changes will take place on the page.

CAMs can also be either systems oriented or stand alone. A stand-alone CAM has within its memory the width values for the type fonts you will be setting. Input may be accomplished directly into the CAM via an attached keyboard, or from some recorded medium.

In some cases the CAM may be connected to a larger computer typesetting system. This usually includes a minicomputer, rigid magnetic disk for storage, video editors and input and output devices. All of these, and multiples of them, are interconnected. The CAM thus becomes a peripheral to this system.

**The future of page makeup** Advances in digitization and scanning now permit us to reduce any visual item (pictures, illustrations, etc.) to a series of digital signals. High resolution video devices can display these elements. Thus CAMs will eventually handle type and other elements routinely. Already, digitized typesetters are setting type and making halftones.

Newly introduced copier/duplicators use digitized methods to produce pages for high-speed reproduction. For the last few years we have been using digitized methods for platemaking, scanning a page pasteup and then using lasers to produce the plate.

The implications of electronic page makeup lead us to the plate and reproduction steps of the printing process. Once a page is in electronic form, it can be stored, transmitted, and output to a typesetter, platemaker or electronic reproduction system. In some cases it may be transmitted by earth-orbiting satellites to remote printing locations.

### Word Processing (WP)

In business offices, word processors are typewriters connected to some form of recorded medium. This permits typists to "capture" keystrokes for editing and correction. The IBM MT/ST was the first word processor and was essentially a typewriter with magnetic tape cartridges that allowed the operator to update and change input copy during or after typing.

Today most word processors are video based and can perform formatting and page layout similar to typesetters. Most importantly, the material being handled may eventually find its way to typesetting. Having the recorded medium thus allows input to typesetting without rekeyboarding.

Output from word processors is usually typewriter-like. Newer high-speed printers using impact, ink jet or electrostatic techniques can simulate typesetting. The electronic nature of word processors links nicely with electronic reproduction systems.

Word processors have evolved into *standalone* (self-contained) units or *shared logic* (multi-terminal systems). The keyboard and video screen is now called a *workstation*. Units that display illustration or formatted data are called *graphic workstations*.

### Telecommunications

Information stored in most electronic text systems may be communicated over telephone lines. *Modems* convert signals from these systems into telephone signals and then re-convert them at the other end. Transmission requirements are called *protocols*, allowing transmission in one direction *(asynchronous)* or in both directions simultaneously *(synchronous)* for error correction. All word processors and personal computers telecommunicate, but only with like models.

### Interfacing

The linking of different electronic devices is called *interfacing*. It may be accomplished by reading a recorded medium, accepting telecommunications, or simply connecting the units by cable. A *converter* is required to translate the *coding system* of one system to another. A *translation table* establishes individual conversions of input codes into new output codes.

### Personal Computers

Usually consisting of keyboard, video screen, floppy disk (and internal microprocessor computer), personal computers have become the Model Ts of the electronics world. Easy-to-change software allows each unit to perform word processing, accounting and other functions for business or personal use. Data prepared on personal computers is often interfaced with typesetting.

# Copy preparation
# Art preparation

The mechanics of typesetting have already been discussed. This section will explain (1) how to prepare manuscript copy for typesetting, and (2) how to prepare art for graphic reproduction.

## COPY PREPARATION FOR TYPESETTING

Good copy preparation and accurate markup insures correct typesetting of manuscript copy with a minimum of alterations, in the shortest possible time, and thus at the lowest cost.

Careful checking and editing of text matter *before* it is set is a must! Remember, the typesetter *must* set copy as it is furnished, even if he/she suspects errors. Therefore, it is of the utmost importance that spelling, punctuation, capitalization, uniformity of style, etc., be carefully checked.

**Paper** Use standard 8½″ x 11″ letter size white bond. This allows for erasures and fits standard file cabinets.

**Typing** should be clean, double-spaced, of uniform width and length, with wide margins, and on one side of the paper only. Typewriters used should have a uniform character count per inch. Make a copy as insurance against loss of the original.

**Identification** should be made at the top of each sheet to prevent possible mixup—title, running head, page number, etc.

**Numbering** Sheets should be numbered consecutively and marked *end* on the last sheet. If a sheet is added or removed after numbering, note it on the preceding page.

**Corrections** should be made above the line wherever possible, in ink—not pencil. If there are many corrections, the page should be retyped. Corrections should *not* be made in the left margin, on the back of the sheet, or on attached slips which may be misplaced or lost.

Simplifying the typesetter's job helps to reduce costs and often expedites delivery. Corrections made in the manuscript are far less costly than *author's alterations* after the type is set.

### Copyfitting

Copyfitting refers to the amount of manuscript copy that can be fit into a given area of a printed piece for a specified size and style of type. Many different copy elements may occupy predetermined areas, and it is the task of the typographer to select the kind and size of type that will do the job best. Book composition presents a different problem in copyfitting. A length estimate is prepared (overall character count of the entire manuscript) and converted into point size, leading, pica measure and line count per page based on a predetermined estimated number of pages in the book.

There are different approaches to the problem of copyfitting. Sometimes the copy is specified in a given type face, size and measure. In this case, it is necessary to estimate the total number of lines paragraph by paragraph. This will determine the total depth of type, or the number of pages it will make.

When copy must be fitted into a given area, there are two basic steps to be taken: (1) the copy must be accurately measured, and (2) that measure must be applied to a specific size of a specific type face.

**Copy measurement** The *character count* method of measuring copy is the most accurate and widely used. This consists of counting the characters and spaces in the typewritten copy, line for line, on a paragraph basis. There are various aids for doing this. The handiest is a ruler calibrated in inches. Standard *pica* typewriters (12-point) have 10 characters to the inch, while the more common *elite* (10-point) have 12 characters to the inch. After the count is completed, the next step is to calculate the area into which it will fit in the selected type face.

**Methods of type calculation** There are type books that list the characters-per-pica of all sizes of the most common type faces. With these charts it is quite simple to calculate the number of characters in a desired size and pica measure of a given type face. By dividing this number into the total number of characters in the copy, paragraph by paragraph, one can determine the total number of lines the copy will make.

For example, if we know that a 20 pica line of 10-point Times Roman has 53 characters, and that the original copy contains 562 characters in one paragraph, by dividing 562 by 53 we get 10+ or 11 lines of type for that paragraph.

**Copy Markup**

The type specifications should be clearly and completely written on the typed manuscript (not the layout) with the size, leading,

TYPICAL COPYFITTING TABLE

## HELVETICA REG., Character Count Per Pica

| Picas ► | 10 | 12 | 14 | 16 | 18 | 20 | 22 | 24 | 26 | 28 | 30 |
|---|---|---|---|---|---|---|---|---|---|---|---|
| **7 pt.** | 32 | 38 | 45 | 51 | 58 | 64 | 70 | 77 | 83 | 90 | 96 |
| **8 pt.** | 29 | 35 | 41 | 46 | 52 | 58 | 64 | 70 | 75 | 81 | 87 |
| **9 pt.** | 27 | 32 | 38 | 43 | 49 | 54 | 59 | 65 | 70 | 76 | 81 |
| **10 pt.** | 24 | 29 | 34 | 38 | 43 | 48 | 53 | 58 | 62 | 67 | 72 |
| **12 pt.** | 20 | 24 | 28 | 32 | 36 | 40 | 44 | 48 | 52 | 56 | 60 |

type face, and measure in that order. In marking the size, the leading (space between lines) should always be specified in the form of a fraction—8/9 (8 on 9) means 8-point type with 1-point leading, 10/10 means 10-point solid (no leading), etc. Leading does not affect the number of lines, only the depth. When a large amount of copy is to be set, care should be used to select a type face that does not require much leading.

Always specify line measure in picas. An example of complete specifications would be: 10/12 Times Roman x 20, which means 10-point Times Roman with 2-point leading to be set in a column 20 picas wide. Indicate if it is to be justified or set flush with a ragged right or left margin.

Careful word spacing is important! It must be remembered that all formulas for copyfitting are based on even word spacing throughout. If a job is widely word spaced, copyfitting calculations may be upset by poor workmanship.

All paragraph indentions, hold-ins, etc., should be indicated in *ems* of the type size—not in picas. (An *em* is the square of the body type, i.e., an 8-point em is 8 points square.) Be sure to indicate whether paragraphs should be indented or kept flush. Mark headings flush left, flush right, centered, and/or indented according to the design.

Underscoring a word or line has a very definite meaning to the typesetter. One underscore means *set in italic*, two mean SET IN ALL SMALL CAPS and three underscores mean SET IN ALL CAPS. Underscore also means "underline" which is done with a rule by typesetter or drawn on a repro, not to be confused with setting italic. Although a wavy underscore means **set in bold face,** it is always better to mark "bf" in the margin.

Again, in order to avoid delays and resetting, always mark up copy fully and accurately, then recheck your work. Accurate copy markup eliminates guessing, expedites delivery, and keeps costs down.

## ART PREPARATION

Having discussed how to prepare manuscript copy for typesetting, the next consideration is art preparation. To the printer, art and copy (not to be confused with manuscript copy) are terms used to describe *all* material supplied for reproduction. It includes not only the type, but also diagrams, drawings, photographs, and color transparencies. Art preparation embraces all of the steps in getting the art and copy ready for reproduction. There are two basic steps: (1) the design or layout of a printed piece, and (2) the preparation and assembly of the various components of this piece for reproduction.

**The Layout**

The first step in the designing of a printed piece is preparing a layout . . . a blueprint of a printed job. It is important that the layout person know the purpose of the printed piece (as well as the printing process to be used) so that the layout will reflect this. The layout may be a very rough visual, a loose comprehensive, or a tightly rendered comprehensive, looking like the finished job in all details. The designer of a booklet or folder will often make several rough sketches (called *roughs*) of the cover and a two-page spread for approval. Then, once approved, often after some changes, proceed with the final layout. The final layout may be crudely drawn, but it must be accurate in size and accurately marked, as it is the blueprint from which all people (including the designer) who will be producing the job will take their specifications.

At the same time the layouts are being prepared, a blank paper dummy of the job should be made to size, preferably on the stock to be used. This will help the designer visualize the final appearance, enabling him/her to provide proper margins, bleeds, color, etc. Attention should be paid to stay within the boundaries of standard paper sizes, the printing process and press size to be used.

With the approved layout and paper dummy to guide him, the artist is ready to put all the elements together into a final pasted-up *mechanical* (or *pasteup*) for graphic reproduction.

ROUGH LAYOUT

COMPREHENSIVE LAYOUT

**Kinds of Original Images**

There are several kinds of original images. In general, they are classified according to whether the copy is *line* as in type matter,

LINE

HALFTONE

diagrams, and pen and ink drawings; or *continuous tone* as in a black-and-white photograph with a variety of tones. These are further broken down as to whether they are to be reproduced in one color, multicolor, or process color, and whether they are alone or in combination (line and continuous tone).

Therefore, we can have either line or continuous-tone images in one color, combinations of line and tone in one color; line or tone in more than one color, combinations of line and tone in more than one color; process color tone images, and combinations of process color tone and line.

Continuous-tone images may be either rendered illustrations or photographs. For reproduction by most printing processes, continuous-tone images are converted to dot pattern images, or

MULTICOLOR MECHANICAL (2nd & 3rd colors on overlays)

*halftones.* Halftones have the appearance of continuous-tone images because of the limited resolving power of the human eye. This limitation accounts for an optical illusion; small half-tone dots when viewed at the normal reading distance cannot be resolved as individual dots, but blend into a continuous tone. *(See illustration, below.)*

## Art for Multicolor Printing

Most art for multicolor reproduction is prepared in black and white on a mechanical. When hairline register is not required, the art for the key color is pasted to a sheet of illustration board, and the art for other colors registered on clear acetate overlays hinged to the board. Color and screened percentages (if any) should be marked on each overlay. This is sometimes called *pre-separated* art. For hairline register all colors should appear on the same board, if possible, and the color break indicated on a tissue overlay. Pin register devices can be used to insure hairline register of separate image elements if they cannot be combined on the same board. Finish size should also be indicated on the art. If several pieces of art are prepared for a job, they should be drawn all the same size. This simplifies camera and preparation costs. All copy should be *keyed* or cross-referenced by page number, title or job number.

In preparing art where two or more colors are to be printed, registration of the different color images is usually an important factor. Where several color areas are completely independent of each other, it is considered a *no-register* job. In 4-color process printing *commercial register* means that slight variations in color images are acceptable (about ± one row of dots); *tight, close* or *hairline register* indicates that the relations must be extremely precise ( ± about ½ row of dots).

HALFTONE DOTS ENLARGED

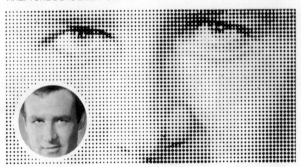

Additional colors and color values can be obtained by over-printing two or more inks. Overprinting can be in both solids and tints (various tones of a solid color). A skillful artist can create a wide variety of colors by this method.

A black-and-white photograph can be reproduced in two colors to obtain more depth or density. This two-color halftone is called a *duotone*. Two closely related colors, black and a complementary color, or even two black inks can be used. The original picture is photographed twice, one negative emphasizing the highlights (lighest parts), and the other, the shadows (darkest parts). Sometimes, a two-color *duotone effect* is used by printing a screened tint of a color over a black halftone. *(See illustrations, page 90.)*

Art for color reproduction falls into two classes: *reflection* and *transmission* copy. Reflection copy is original material for reproduction which is viewed and photographed by reflected light, such as oil paintings and photographic color prints.

Transmission copy, such as color transparencies and color negatives, are viewed and photographed by transmitted light.

REFLECTION COPY

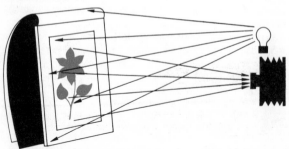

TRANSMISSION COPY

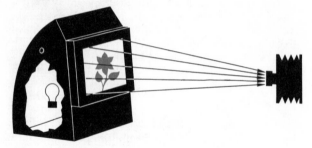

## Scaling and Cropping

Many different original art elements may be used in producing a printed piece. Some may have to be reduced or enlarged in size, which requires *scaling* and *cropping*. Scaling has to do with changing the size of the original without changing the ratio of the dimensions (*see illustration*). In addition to the diagonal line

DIAGONAL LINE METHOD OF SCALING

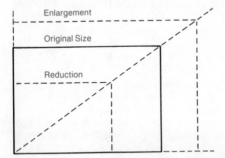

method of reproduction size, a printer's proportion scale can easily determine a reproduction size. Cropping is a term meaning to eliminate certain areas from the picture.

## Assembling Art and Copy

The mechanical (pasteup) is the final assembly of art and copy elements into a unit for photomechanical reproduction. This includes all art and copy, except for black-and-white halftones or full color reproduction which is handled separately. The mechanical is prepared on a white board with all the line copy pasted in position, and with trim, folds and bleeds indicated. The bleed extends past the margin and beyond the trim. It is usually 1/8". The space allotted for halftones is drawn with a black keyline or blocked out with a red acetate-backed material. This is called para-opaquing and creates a window in the line negative which is photo-converted with the line copy. All copy must be clean, free of dirt and damage.

   In preparing art for the camera, line images must be separated from continuous-tone images. Photographically they belong to different groups. Images for full-color reproduction form a third group. Images that are not assembled together must be cross-referenced for easy identification. This operation is called *keying*. This can be done by making an outline drawing of the image on the mechanical or by photostats which are pasted where key images will appear. Images keyed for color may be indicated by

MECHANICAL, SHOWING POSITION OF ART AND COPY

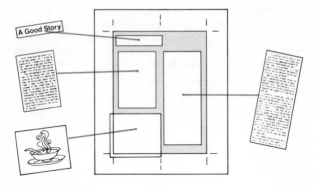

different color areas drawn on a tissue overlay on the mechanical.

Traditionally, letterpress printing has been from metal type and photoengravings assembled by skilled craftsmen, rather than camera-ready mechanicals prepared by commercial artists for offset lithography. Layouts consist of type and engraver's proofs, pasted together in position for printing.

Gravure requires extensive assembly of art and copy as each element is handled separately. Each method of cylinder preparation handles copy differently. As a rule, type images are not exposed to the carbon tissue (sensitized gelatin transfer medium) with continuous-tone images.

Screen printing art and copy can be prepared either manually with the knife-cut film method, photomechanically, or by a combination of both these methods.

### Duplicate Films and Prints

In color reproduction original copy is usually supplied piecemeal, and it must often be reproduced at different enlargements. Color separating and correcting each separately results in considerable manual color film assembly or stripping. One method of reducing the time-consuming and expensive manual operations is to make duplicate films on special color films, like Kodak Ektachrome E-6, of each of the color originals at correct size and cropping, and assembling them in exact position so the assembly can be color separated and corrected as a single unit. With the availability of easily produced diffusion transfer color print materials like Kodak *Ektaflex PCT* and Agfa-Gevaert CopyColor *(see page 78)*, there is a trend toward using duplicate color prints in the same manner as duplicate films. The color prints have the advantage that they look more like the printed result than the color films.

# Graphic arts photography

To the printer, there are two types of photography: *creative* and *graphic arts.* Creative photography provides original images for reproduction and is a product of commercial photographers, art studios, and creative art departments in printing companies. Graphic arts photography is used in the reproduction of art and copy, and is an integral part of the printing process.

## GRAPHIC ARTS PHOTOGRAPHY

### Negatives and Positives

The materials used in graphic arts photography are similar to those for creative photography. Light-sensitive photographic materials consist of: (1) a base which may be paper, plastic film or glass, and (2) a light-sensitive coating known as *photographic emulsion,* which is composed essentially of silver salts (halides) in gelatin.

The usual product of the photographic process is a *negative* in which the light portions of the copy are represented by heavy or dark deposits of silver, and the dark portions of the copy are light or transparent. When negatives are printed on paper or film they produce *positives* in which the tone values are similar to what they were on the original copy. Some platemaking processes require negatives, others require positives.

Letterpress plates are always made from negatives. Positives are used for gravure. Some lithographic plate processes use negatives, others use positives. Screen printing requires positives. Negatives or positives can be line, continuous tone or halftone, straight reading or reverse reading on the emulsion side depending on the process and use.

### Continuous Tone vs. Halftone

Any photograph, wash drawing, oil painting, etc. consisting of a broad range of tones or gradation of tones is known as *continuous tone.* In creative photography these different tones are represented by varying amounts of silver. This metallic silver appears black in the photographic emulsion; it does not look at all like silver. The more silver, the darker the image, and vice versa.

In letterpress and offset lithography, tones cannot be reproduced by varying the amounts of ink. These printing processes can print only a solid density of a color in the image areas, while no ink prints in the non-image areas. In order to reproduce the varying tones of a picture, graphic arts photography uses a halftone screen. Halftone photography makes the printing of continuous-tone photographs possible by converting the continuous-tone image into a pattern of very small and clearly defined *dots* of varying sizes. The *halftone principle* is an optical illusion in which tones are represented by a large number of small dots of different sizes with equal spacing printed with ink of uniform thickness (density) *(see illustration, page 67).*

Some printing processes are capable of printing varying ink densities to produce pictures having a wide range of tones without the need for halftones. Conventional gravure is one. Even though a screen is used, all wells are the same shape and size but they vary in depth so different amounts of ink are printed according to the tone values to be printed. Another process is collotype in which the image consists of reticulated gelatin which prints ink density in proportion to the amount of exposure the gelatin has received through a continuous-tone negative. Screenless lithography has also been used in which the plates are made lithographically from continuous-tone negatives or positives *(see page 135).*

## Graphic Arts Cameras

A graphic arts camera consists of: copyboard, lensboard, lens, bellows, camera back, and independent camera bed or suspension. The copyboard serves to position the original copy. Many have transparency holders so they can accommodate both reflection and transmission copy. Most cameras are of the darkroom type. Their front ends, consisting of bellows, lens and copyboard, are in the camera area; the camera back or image plane is built into a wall of the darkroom.

There are horizontal or vertical cameras. Horizontal cameras can have either floor-type or over-head suspension. In overhead units, the components are suspended from one or more beams supported by tall uprights from the floor. The suspension sys-

FLOOR-TYPE HORIZONTAL CAMERA

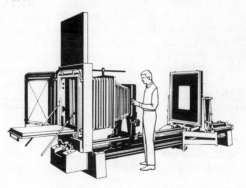

tems are designed to eliminate effects of vibration on the images, during exposure. Vertical cameras save space. Enlargers, a form of vertical camera, are used for making color separations in the direct screen process for color reproduction.

**Lenses** are coated and usually of symmetrical design to eliminate distortion in the images. High resolution and minimum aberrations are essential. All process lenses are *apochromatic,* or fully corrected for the visible spectrum. Lenses have fairly small maximum apertures, ranging from f/8 to f/11. (Note: The larger the f/no. the smaller the lens opening and the longer the exposure.) Focal lengths range from 8″ for wide angle lenses for 20″ cameras (20″ square images), to as long as 48″ for a 40″ camera. (A 35mm camera has a 2″ focal length lens.)

**Lights**  Because of the slow exposure speed of the high contrast, high resolution films used for graphic arts, high intensity lights or lamps are needed for exposure. Carbon arc lamps were used extensively, but these were variable in light output due to uneven burning rates of carbon arcs. These lamps have gradually been replaced with *pulsed Xenon* lamps for color reproduction and *quartz iodine* lamps for single color reproduction. *Photoflood* lamps are used for some photography. For contact printing special *point source* lights are used.

**Exposure controls** *Light integrators* are used to control exposures in photography and platemaking. They integrate the total quantity of light by varying the time as intensity changes. With the introduction of computers, sophisticated exposure control devices have been developed for use on cameras, enlargers and special systems to make color separations, enlargements and reductions, contact screen main, flash and bump exposures, etc.

**Film**  Stable base films are used where dimensional stability is critical, as in color separation photography. Special high contrast emulsions of silver halides in gelatin, known as *lithfilm,* are used for line and halftone photography. Continuous-tone film is used for color separations, masks and gravure printing. Special films are made for scanners, and new special *daylight* films are available for contact printing for *stripping* or *image assembly.* Films are color sensitized. Ordinary or colorblind film is sensitive to ultraviolet (UV) and blue light. Orthochromatic film is sensitive to UV, blue and green light. Panchromatic film is sensitive to UV, blue, green and red light *(see illustration, next page).*

**Development**  During exposure a latent image is formed in the gelatino-silver halide emulsion which is made visible by immersing it in a special *developer* that converts the silver

COMPARISON OF COLOR SENSITIVITY
OF EYE AND PHOTOGRAPHIC FILMS

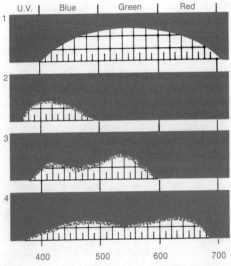

1. Sensitivity of the human eye
2. Ordinary color-blind film
3. Orthochromatic film
4. Panchromatic film

halide to metallic silver in proportion to the amount of exposure received. Each film type uses special developing agents and combinations of chemicals. Developing time and temperature are means of control used to get desired results. After development the action of the developer is stopped by immersing the film in an acid stop bath or plain water. The film is then immersed in a fixing bath which uses sodium or ammonia thiosulfate, or *hypo*, to convert the unexposed silver halide to a soluble complex which is dissolved in the water wash after the fixing. Washing is important because stains will form if it is incomplete.

*Stabilization* processing eliminates washing by converting the unexposed silver halide to a stable complex which eventually stains on exposure to sufficient extraneous light. *Rapid Access* processing using continuous-tone type developers has been introduced to speed up development of lith films in automatic processors with electronically-generated (laser) images.

An important trend since 1960 has been the increased use of *automatic film processing* machines. These machines process all types of films, and not only save considerable time but produce more consistent results. Film is developed, fixed, washed and dried in less time than it used to take just to develop.

## Line Photography

Line copy consists of solids, lines, figures, and text matter. The copy is placed on the copyboard, and the film is placed in the vacuum back of the camera. The correct size image is focused by adjusting the bellows extension and copyboard extension. To check focus, a ground glass is placed in the same position as the vacuum back. The lens aperture is set, and an exposure is made through the shutter operated manually by a stopwatch or automatically by a time or light integrator. The copy is illuminated by high intensity lights. Usually an orthochromatic film is used. Processing the film produces a negative.

**Contact printing** Considerable *contacting* of negatives or positives is required in film assembly. Contact prints are made by placing a negative or positive over an unexposed piece of film (usually color-blind) in a vacuum frame, then exposing it to a light source. The resulting contact print will be a positive if made from a negative, or a negative if made from a positive. However, it is possible to make negatives from negatives or positives from positives by using special duplicating film. Most contacting is now done with special daylight films which have low sensitivity and allow contacts to be made outside the darkroom.

## HALFTONE PHOTOGRAPHY

Halftone photography is done through the grid pattern of a halftone screen. There are two types of screens: *glass* and *contact*. A glass screen consists of two sheets of glass, each ruled by precision equipment with a given number of lines per linear inch. Lines are approximately equal in width to the spaces between them. The two sheets of glass are cemented together at right angles to each other. The number of lines per inch is designated as the screen ruling. Common screen rulings are: 65- to 85-line for newspapers by letterpress; 100-, 120- and 133-line for offset newspapers; 120-, 133- and 150-line for magazines and commercial letterpress; 133- and 150-line for offset lithography. Finer screen rulings such as 200-line and 300-line are used in color reproduction by offset lithography.

A contact screen is on a film base and is usually made from a glass screen. Dots are vignetted with variable density across each dot. Density is greatest at the center and least at the perimeter. There are gray screens with dots consisting of silver images. Dyed screens, usually magenta, contain dots in which the silver has been replaced by a dye. There are also square and elliptical

ENLARGED GLASS SCREEN          ENLARGED CONTACT SCREEN

dot screens for special effects, especially in the middle tones and Respi *(see Graphic Arts terms)* and ''triple dot'' screens for special effects in the highlights.

## Glass Screen Photography

Photography with a glass screen is decreasing in use. It is done by placing the screen a precise short distance in front of the film in the back of the camera which requires an expensive screen holder. During exposure, the light reflected or transmitted from the copy is projected through the transparent spaces of the screen, which act as pinhole lenses to produce dots on the film proportional in size to the amount of light reflected from the copy. Screen distance, lens aperture, and length of exposure are very critical as they affect contrast and tone reproduction.

## Contact Screen Photography

Photography with a contact screen is much simpler than with a glass screen. The screen is used in direct contact with the film. The variable density of the vignetted dots records variations as larger or smaller dots on the film, depending upon the amount of light reflected or transmitted from the copy. Contrast of reproduction can be varied within limits by techniques known as *flashing* and *no-screen* exposure. Flash exposures are used to reduce contrast especially in the shadows by producing a dot over the whole film and are made by exposing the film to a yellow bulb or light. The no-screen or *bump* exposure is used for increasing the contrast in the highlights and is done by removing the screen during a short part of the exposure. Additional control of contrast may be achieved with dyed screens by using colored filters during part of the exposure.

MAKING A HALFTONE NEGATIVE

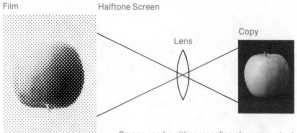

Film                          Halftone Screen

Lens

Copy

*Screen can be either crossline glass or contact.*

**Screened prints** are used with other line copy in pasteups that can be photographed as a line shot, thus eliminating the need for stripping-in halftone negatives. The technique, known as *copy-dot* reproduction, is used for printing newspapers, house organs, school annuals, real estate catalogs and other types of work where ease of makeup is desirable and speed is essential. In making screened prints, tone values are deliberately distorted to compensate for the sharpening of highlights and filling-in of shadows in photography.

Screened prints can be produced by making contact prints from halftone negatives on high contrast photographic paper. The most direct method is to use *diffusion transfer* materials like Kodak *PMT,* Agfa-Gevaert *Copy-Rapid* or Polaroid which consist of two parts–a negative material on which the exposure is made, and a receiver sheet to which the positive image is transferred during processing.

**Color diffusion transfer prints** are new diffusion transfer color print materials like Polaroid, Kodak *Ektaflex PCT* and Agfa-Gevaert *CopyColor* which are used for making second original color prints for pasteup layouts for scanning *(see page 70).*

**Contrast and Tone Reproduction**

Using a stepped gray scale to represent the tones in a subject, good tone reproduction results when the darkest area prints on the press as a solid and the lightest area prints without a dot. The films may have very small unprintable dots in these areas which close up in the shadows and disappear in the highlights during printing. Intermediate tones have varying sizes of dots ranging from about 5% in the highlight area to about 90% in the shadows. Some smooth printing plates can print dots as fine as 2-3% in the highlights and 95% in the shadows, on smooth coated paper and under good conditions of printing.

*High contrast* results when two or three steps in the shadow end print solid and several steps in the highlight end are white with a corresponding increase in density difference between other steps of the scale.

*Low contrast* results when the scale contains 80-90% dots in the shadows and 10-20% dots in the highlights with corresponding decrease in density difference between other steps in the scale. A number of special techniques may be used to change the contrast in local areas of the reproduction.

## COLOR REPRODUCTION

Color reproduction is based on the theory of three-color vision. White light, which contains the wavelengths of all light has three primary colors; blue, green, and red. This is the psychological concept of color as distinguished from the physical one in which each wavelength of light varies in color from every other. The eye contains three different types of receptors, each sensitive to one of the primary colors of light. When the eye views a color scene, the receptors are activated by the colors to which they are sensitive and impulses are sent to the brain. The brain recreates the scene from the transmitted impulses.

The three colors, blue, green and red, are called *additive primaries* because three lights of these colors when added together produce white light.

### Color Separation

The process of color separation is analogous to the process of seeing by the eye. The original photo or artwork is photographed using three filters, each corresponding in color and light transmission to one of the additive primaries.

Placing a red filter over the lens produces a negative recording of all the red light reflected or transmitted from the subject. This is known as the red separation negative. When a positive or print is made from this negative, the silver in the film will correspond to areas which did *not* contain red but contained the other two colors of light, which are blue and green. In effect, the negative has subtracted the red light from the scene and the positive is a recording of the blue and green in the scene which is called *cyan*. The positive is the *cyan printer*.

Photography through the green filter produces a negative recording of the green in the original. The positive is a recording of the other additive primaries, red and blue, which is called *magenta*. The positive is the *magenta printer*.

The blue filter produces a negative recording of all the blue in the subject. The positive records the red and green which when combined as additive colors produce *yellow*. This positive is the *yellow printer*.

These three colors, cyan, magenta, and yellow are called *subtractive primaries* because each represents two additive primaries left after one primary has been subtracted from white light. These are the colors of the process inks used for process color reproduction.

When the three positives are combined and printed, the result should be a reasonable reproduction of the original. Unfortunately, it is not. The colors, outside of yellow and red, are dirty and muddied. There is too much yellow in the magentas, purples and blues, and too much magenta in the greens, blues and cyans. This is not a flaw in the theory but is due to deficiencies in the colors of the pigments used in the inks.

Corrections must be made in the color separation negatives and positives to overcome the limitations in the colors of the inks. Even after these corrections are made, the printed result is not satisfactory, because it lacks full contrast.

A fourth, *black printer*, is added to overcome this. It improves the contrast of the grays and deep shadows and it may be a skeleton or a full black. There is a trend toward the use of full blacks, especially on high-speed magazine printing. Other colors are reduced proportionately so that inks transfer or *trap* properly on high-speed presses. This operation of reducing colors and printing a full black in shadow areas is called *undercolor removal*.

## Color Correction

Corrections to compensate for the spectral errors in inks are done manually, photographically and electronically.

**Dot etching**   When done manually, corrections to increase or reduce color in local areas are made in halftone negatives or positives by reducing the size of the dots with chemical reducers. This is called *dot etching*. Reducing dot sizes in negatives increases color and in positives reduces it. Dots in metal halftone plates for letterpress or gravure may be etched locally after the plates have been made. This is called *fine etching* or *re-etching*.

**Masking**   When color corrections are made photographically, the operation is called *masking*. Numerous methods are used. The most common method is *negative masking* in which two or three low density negatives are made of the original through special filters. Each is a mask placed in contact with the original (transparency) or in the back of the camera (reflection copy) when separations are made. The masks correct color in the separation negatives in proportion to the strengths of the masks. In *indirect color separation* continuous-tone corrected separation negatives are made which are used to make screen positives in a camera.

**Direct screening** is the simplest photographic method of color separation and correction which produces color corrected halftone separations directly. This method can be used by contact or projection for transparency copy and by projection for reflection copy. One or two negative masks are used, depending on the subject and the amount and type of correction needed. In contact and projection printing of transparencies, the masks are registered to the transparency and the color and tone corrected screen separation is made using a gray contact screen and special halftone film. For reflection copy, different masks are used and the mask is placed over the screen in the back of the camera (whence the term *camera back masking*). Special targets are used that have three aim points in the highlight, middle tone and shadow ends of the scale to ensure proper tone reproduction in the halftone separations. This system is so simple and comprehensive that a number of special enlargers and exposure computer systems have been developed for its use.

**Electronic scanning** is rapidly becoming the system of choice for color separation and correction. Separation is accomplished by scanning the original with a light beam that is split into three beams after passing through, or being reflected from, the original. Each beam goes to a photocell covered with a filter that

PRINCIPLE OF AN ELECTRONIC SCANNER

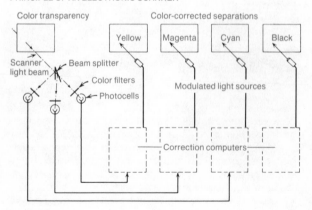

corresponds to one of the additive primaries, thus separating each area of the copy into its three color components *(see illustration)*. Color correction is done by feeding electrical currents from the photocells into four separate computers, one for each color and one for the black which is computed from the other three signals. The computers can be reset to modify currents depending on the inks, paper, tonal range and other printing conditions. The modified currents are fed to exposing lights which vary in intensity in proportion to the corrected value of each element in the area scanned as they expose the corrected color separations on film. Some scanners produce one or two color-corrected separations at a time. Analog to digital converters enlarge or reduce the image; contact screens or electronic dot generators with lasers produce halftone images directly. The newest scanners use digital computers for both color correction and screening and are modular with input and output in separate units.

## Screen Angles

In multicolor printing there is a problem which is not usually present in single-color halftone or in multicolor screenless printing. This is the occurrence of an undesirable *moiré* (pronounced moa-wray) pattern when multicolor halftone images are not properly angled when printed. The printed image will show a pattern that interferes with its appearance.

MOIRÉ PATTERNS

 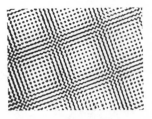

By proper angling of halftone screens moiré patterns can be reduced. A minimum pattern is formed when an angle of 30° between screens is used. Since the commonly used halftone screens consist of line rulings or dot patterns at 90° to each other, there is room for only three 30° angles before they repeat. In four-color printing, two of the colors must be printed at the same angle or must be separated by other than 30°. As a rule, because yellow is a light color, it is printed at an angle of 15° from two other colors, generally cyan and magenta. Usual screen angles are: black, 45°;

magenta, 75°; yellow, 90°; and cyan, 105° *(see illustration, page 96).* An error as small as 0.1° between screen angles or a slight misregister between colors can cause serious moiré in areas where three and four colors overprint.

A moiré pattern can also be caused by improper transfer of ink, a condition called *poor trapping.* Proper trapping occurs when the same amount of ink transfers to both the previously printed and unprinted areas of the paper. If inks are not formulated to trap properly, the print will have weak overprint colors (red, blue and green) and accentuated moiré patterns.

### Pre-Separated Color Printing (Fake Color Process)

This type of color printing is usually produced from a black-and-white photograph or wash drawing. Various areas of the original are translated into colors which are reproduced with process inks. Usually the design studio will specify the desired colors by indicating halftone percentages for different areas of the reproduction; sometimes the printer or photoengraver will use trained specialists for this type of work. A number of color charts are available to be used as guides to determine approximate dot percentages for printing required colors.

### COLOR PROOFING

The main purposes of proofing are to see if all the elements fit, and are in the right color, and how the job will look when it is printed. Most color separations are proofed to determine the accuracy of corrections, whether more corrections are needed, or whether there are serious errors requiring a makeover. After correction most of them are reproofed and shown to the customer for approval. A third proof is usually made when the job is finally assembled and ready for platemaking. Two types of color proofing systems are in use: *press* and *off-press.* Press proofs are more expensive as they require a press and printing plates or cylinders; off-press proofs are made directly from the corrected films.

All processes use off-press color proofing systems as quality control checks of camera and scanner separation and correction operations. When it comes to showing a proof to the customer, letterpress and gravure use press proofs almost exclusively, mainly because the chemical etching involved in making plates and cylinders affects tone reproduction and correction. Lithography, however, can use more off-press proofing because the films and plates have essentially the same tone reproduction characteristics.

While production presses can be used for making proofs, most press proofing is done on special presses. The main advantages of press proofs are the ability to proof with the actual printing inks on the printing paper and the ease of producing progressive proofs and quantities of proofs particularly for advertising agencies. Their disadvantages are the time it takes to make them and their cost.

There are two types of off-press proofs: *overlay* and *integral*. Overlay proofs like 3M *Color Key*, Enco *NAPS* and *PAPS*, and Polychrome *Chrome-Guide* are simple and economic to make, but because they consist of four separate films the internal light reflections when viewing them cause graying of whites and light tones. Integral systems like DuPont *Cromalin,* Agfa-Gevaert *GevaProof*, 3M *Transfer Key* and *Matchprint*, K&E *SPECTRA* and *KC-Color Proof* come closer to matching the press print in appearance, but all except KC and SPECTRA use special bases or substrates which do not look or feel like the printing paper. For lithography these proofs are being accepted by many customers as final proofs. Cromalin, KC and SPECTRA are being considered and used as preliminary proofs for gravure.

## NON-SILVER PHOTOGRAPHIC SYSTEMS

There are a number of non-silver photographic systems but none has the speed of silver halide. These systems include vesicular films like Kalvar, diazo and photopolymer coatings, and electrophotographic systems like Xerography and Electrofax. Vesicular films are used for contact exposures and the Converkal conversion process for making negatives from letterpress engravings. Diazo coatings are used in photography for contact films and for blueprinting. There are films with photopolymer coatings that can be used for contact exposures in daylight and can be processed in 20 seconds.

Xerography and Electrofax are used mainly for copying and proofing and for making plates for duplicators. A new electrophotographic system, KC, has been developed which has exposure speed similar to lithfilms. It consists of cadmium sulphide crystals on a polyester or metal base with very high resolution and panchromatic sensitivity. KC materials are used for lithographic plates, for copying, and to produce microfilm, graphic arts film and color proofs.

---

*The following 12 pages illustrate many photomechanical treatments in both black-and-white and color. Included are various types and screenings of halftones, special line screens, the principle and demonstration of four-color process printing, and color process charts.* *The text is continued on page 98.*

# GRADATION AND MAGNIFICATION OF TONES

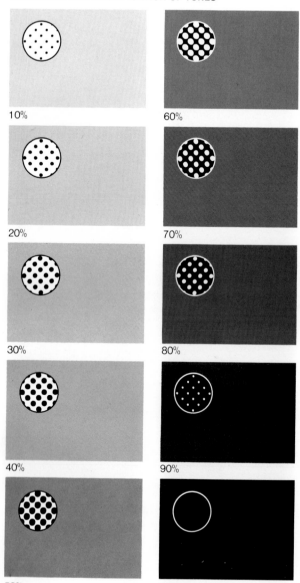

10%

60%

20%

70%

30%

80%

40%

90%

50%

100%

**HALFTONE SCREENS**

65 LINE SCREEN

100 LINE SCREEN

150 LINE SCREEN

**TYPES OF HALFTONES**

HIGH CONTRAST HALFTONE

VIGNETTE HALFTONE

OUTLINE HALFTONE

## SPECIAL LINE SCREENS

STRAIGHT LINE

MEZZO TINT

ETCH TONE

DRY BRUSH

RANDOM LINE

TWO COLOR TEXTURE

**DUOTONES**

STANDARD DUOTONE

DUOTONE EFFECT

**TINTS AND TYPE**

| 50% COLOR | 30% COLOR | 10% COLOR |

White Type Dropout / Black Type Overprint

BLACK HALFTONE OVER COLOR

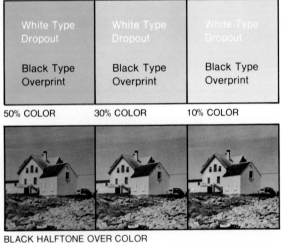

| 50% COLOR | 30% COLOR | 10% COLOR |

White Type Dropout / Black Type Overprint

BLACK HALFTONE OVER COLOR

| 50% BLACK | 30% BLACK | 10% BLACK |

# FOUR COLOR PROCESS PRINTING

BLUE FILTER / YELLOW PRINTER

GREEN FILTER / MAGENTA PRINTER

RED FILTER / CYAN PRINTER

MODIFIED FILTER / BLACK PRINTER

**ROTATION OF COLORS**

YELLOW

YELLOW & MAGENTA

YELLOW, MAGENTA & CYAN

YELLOW, MAGENTA, CYAN & BLACK

**94**

## TWO COLOR PROCESS CHARTS

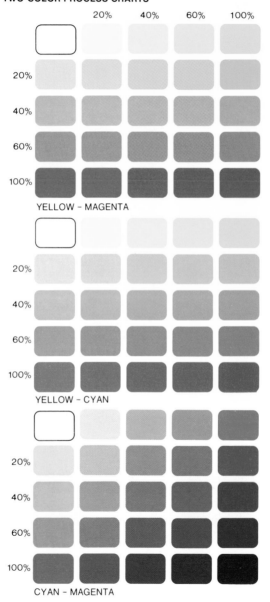

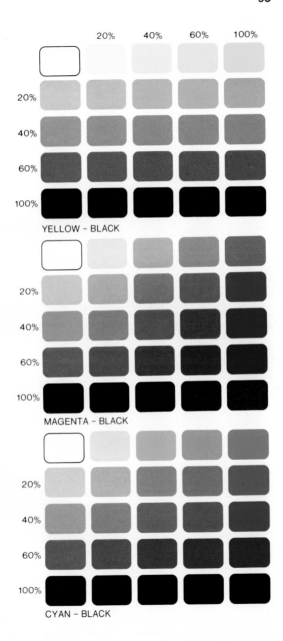

YELLOW – BLACK

MAGENTA – BLACK

CYAN – BLACK

**FOUR COLOR PROCESS** MAGNIFIED DOT PATTERN

**FOUR COLOR PROCESS** HALFTONE SCREEN ANGLES

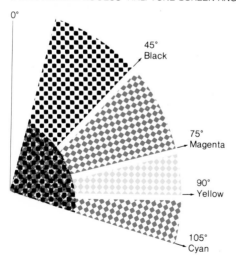

0°

45°
Black

75°
Magenta

90°
Yellow

105°
Cyan

# Film assembly
# and imposition

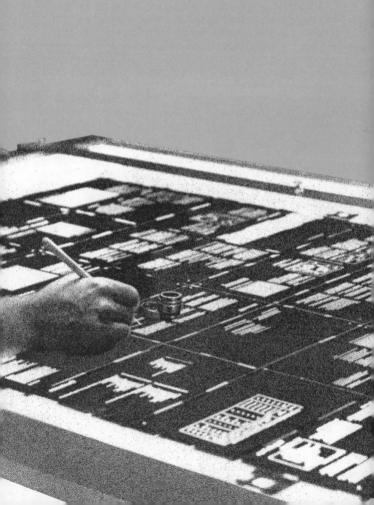

The terms *film assembly*, and *imposition* are essentially synonymous as they both refer to the planned assembly of images for printing. The term imposition originated in letterpress and is still used although it has been replaced in photomechanical processes, like lithography and gravure, by the term *stripping*. The important fact to be stressed is that both imposition and stripping depend on a plan for the assembly of the images for printing. In the photomechanical processes, the plan is often referred to as a press layout (not to be confused with an *art* layout), while the term imposition is still used in letterpress.

This layout, or imposition, usually prepared by the bindery, is needed at the planning stage when a number of pages are to be printed in the same form. This is to insure that when the sheet is printed, folded and trimmed, the pages will appear in the proper sequence. Some presses print single pages and others print multiples of the same subjects such as labels and packaging. In any case, all material for printing must be planned to appear in the proper position for finishing.

## RETOUCHING, OPAQUING AND REGISTERING

After negatives or positives have been made, the individual films must be properly prepared before they can be assembled to make plates. For conventional gravure, the continuous-tone negatives and positives are retouched so they have the proper tone values for printing. For halftone gravure, letterpress and lithography, and for line drawings and text, the films are trimmed, marked for register, margins, bleeds, etc.

Camera negatives of line copy, such as type or line drawings, contain pinholes and other flaws. These are covered over with an application of a special preparation called *opaque,* so they do not print when a contact print or plate is made from the film. The operation is usually called *spotting* and is done on a light table. The opaquer or stripper also does squaring and outlining of halftones as well as contacting film elements to produce a final composite image on film. He may add *register marks* to indicate the correct fit for successive images and *trim marks* as guides for folding and trimming the printed sheet.

**Pin register systems** In addition to register marks, films are most commonly registered now by the use of pin register systems. These consist of devices for punching holes and slots in films and copy, and pins which fit in the holes or slots so the copy or several pieces of film can be held to assure exposure or placement in the correct position. Pin bars in which pins are spaced at the same distance as the holes in the film are used for making multiple exposures on films or plates. Pin register devices are important for color reproduction and are used throughout the pre-press process from the original copy to mounting the plates on the press.

## FILM ASSEMBLY OR STRIPPING

For photomechanical platemaking as used for lithography, gravure, wraparound letterpress, and photopolymer plates, the negatives representing the printing images are taped in position on a sheet of plastic or colored paper *(goldenrod)*. This assembly of films in position is called a *flat*. When all film is in place, the stripper cuts windowed spaces from the goldenrod permitting light to pass through the image areas during exposure.

Layouts or imposition will vary among printers, because of variations in the type and size of printing and binding equipment. For special jobs, the layout should be prepared by, or checked with, the bindery to make sure it can be processed in the folding or other finishing equipment. However, certain basic rules are followed. After page size has been determined, 1/8″ to 1/4″ is added on the top, side and bottom for trim. If the page numbers or folios are not already on the film, they are inserted at this point. On larger signatures, the center or gutter margin is varied according to the position of the page in the signature and the bulk of the paper. This is called *shingling*.

The stripper checks all negatives carefully for opaquing, dimensions, register and cut marks, position and layout. He/she also puts together all elements on a page if they are in separate pieces. If positives are needed for deep-etch, some bimetal plates, and gravure cylinders, contact exposures on film are made of the individual negatives or stripped up flats depending on the particular use or application.

There are three basic types of arrangement of pages for printing: (1) *sheetwise*; (2) *work-and-turn*; and (3) *work-and-tumble*. In sheetwise layouts, different pages are printed on each side of the sheet. It is used when the number of pages to be printed is large enough to fill both sides of the sheet.

In both work-and-turn and work-and-tumble layouts, the front and back of the sheet are printed on the same form, and there are two finished units to the sheet. In work-and-turn, after the first side is printed, the sheet is turned over from left to right for the printing of the second side. The same gripper edge is used for printing both sides; the side guide changes. In work-and-tumble, after the first side is printed, the sheet is turned over from gripper edge to back for the printing of the second side; side guide remains the same. After printing, the sheet is cut in half for folding. Changing the gripper edge and/or side guide can cause problems in register unless the paper is accurately squared and trimmed before printing.

Books and magazines are printed in units of a number of pages per sheet called *signatures*. There may be from 2 to 64 pages on each side of the sheet, depending on the size of the page, the signature and form to be printed.

**Automated stripping**  Since stripping is a manual operation, it is time-consuming and labor intensive, making it very expensive. New developments in stripping, especially in work with repetitive layouts like book printing, are the use of special projection devices for assembling images for reproduction. One projection system (Opti-Copy) uses a camera with a special back which has accurate control of movements in both directions. Completely composed units or pages are placed on a copyboard and photographed so that each exposure is on the optical axis of the lens. The back is moved, so that the unit or page appears in its proper position. Some of these units are used as *step and repeat* machines *(see page 114)*.

In another type of projection system, the units or pages are reduced to 1/4-1/8 in size on microfilm and reprojected back to correct size on a plate in the proper order and correct position for printing. Such systems result in considerable savings in film costs, but have the disadvantage that halftones finer than 133-line cannot be reproduced. Other automated systems for stripping are the CAD/CAM layout systems described in the next chapter *(page 109)*.

## IMPOSITION

In *letterpress,* the pages or image elements must be combined as in stripping, but it is done with metal type and photoengraved illustrations instead of film. As in offset, an imposition layout or diagram is made showing how the pages must be arranged to produce the proper result after folding. For printing on a flat-bed press, the metal type and photoengraved images are assembled into page form, arranged in proper position on an imposing stone, and locked up in a chase that is mounted on the bed of a press. An optical pre-register device is sometimes used in lockup which is more accurate and saves time. For printing on a rotary press, curved electrotypes or stereotypes are mounted on the cylinder of a press in proper position. Mounter-Proofers are used for checking imposition in flexography.

The layouts shown on the following pages illustrate the most common impositions for 4, 6, 8, 12 and 16 page forms. X indicates the gripper edge.

**FOUR PAGE FOLDER**
Work and Turn

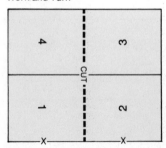

**SIX PAGE FOLDER**
Work and Tumble

**EIGHT PAGE FORM**
Work and Turn
one parallel, one right angle fold

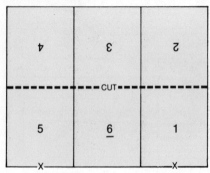

## EIGHT PAGE FORM
Work and Tumble
two parallel folds

| 3 | 9̄ | 7 | 2 |
|---|---|---|---|
| — — — — — — — — — CUT — — — — — — — — — | | | |
| 4 | 5 | 8 | 1 |
| x | | | x |

## TWELVE PAGE FORM
Work and Turn
two parallel (accordian), one right angle fold

| 12 | 1 | 2 | 11 |
|---|---|---|---|
| 9̄ | 4 | 3 | 10 |
| 8 | 5 | 6 | 7 |
| x | | | x |

**SIXTEEN PAGE FORM**
Work and Turn
three right angle folds

|  | 3 | 14 | 15 | 2 |
| X | 6 | 11 | 10 | 7 |
| | | | CUT | |
| | 5 | 12 | 9 | 8 |
| X | 4 | 13 | 16 | 1 |

**EIGHT PAGE HALF-WEB FORM**
one parallel, one right angle fold

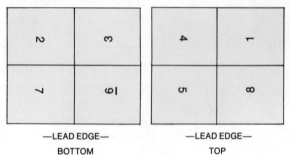

| 2 | 3 | 4 | 1 |
| 7 | 16 | 5 | 8 |

—LEAD EDGE—   —LEAD EDGE—
BOTTOM        TOP

## SIXTEEN PAGE FULL-WEB FORM
three right angle folds

| 13 | 4 | 1 | 16 |
|----|----|----|----|
| 12 | 5 | 8 | <u>9</u> |

—LEAD EDGE—

TOP

| 15 | 2 | 3 | 14 |
|----|----|----|----|
| 10 | 7 | <u>6</u> | 11 |

—LEAD EDGE—

BOTTOM

# Electronic pre-press
systems

The pre-press areas of copy preparation, typesetting, photography and film assembly involve mostly intricate manual operations which are time consuming and expensive, and require highly skilled craftsmen. Because of this, these areas have been the most serious bottlenecks to production. So to shorten lead times and reduce production costs, most of the developments in the industry in recent years have been targeted at the pre-press area. While the industry has been faced with these ills for a long time, the means for curing them were not available until the arrival of the computer. As in other industries the spread of automation in printing has closely paralleled the advancements in computer science—particularly the introduction of the microcomputer, expanded memories and software.

Trends in the last decade have been directed toward integration of most pre-press functions into comprehensive systems. Color scanners and black and white digitizers allow almost every type of visual material to be converted into electronic signals. New, expanded memory techniques permit magnetic storage of millions of bits of data with rapid, direct access.

Laser and array operated electronic cameras are converting images to digital *bits* and *bytes* and could eventually make photographic film obsolete. Color originals are not only being separated and corrected on electronic scanners but the digitized information is being manipulated by software in electronic page composition systems so that completed pages are composed with the pictures corrected and balanced and in exact position with the text. Electronic layout systems using computer aided design and computer aided makeup (CAD/CAM) techniques eliminate much of the handwork of film assembly by producing completely composed layouts on film or rubilith type materials ready for mounting the image films.

## TYPOGRAPHIC FRONT END SYSTEMS

Advances in typographic pagination allow pages of type and rule lines to be produced in position. *Batch* pagination takes text and commands and automatically creates page formats according to pre-set instructions. It works in a *background* mode, blind to the operator. Other pagination devices work in the *foreground*, since they allow interactive pagination on a video screen *(see page 54)*.

Newer video screens and related hardware and software now permit type and black-and-white images to be merged. Newspaper-oriented systems have led developments in this area, directing this technology toward *laser platemakers* which would eliminate the manual steps of page pasteup and negative/plate production. *Computer-to-plate* is the name given to this approach, essentially combining the functions of typesetting, camera photography and contact platemaking.

The video screen has become the "pasteup page" of the graphic arts. Some screens only display a portion of the page, electronically *zooming* the screen image to show a smaller representation (to see the entire page) or a larger entity for manipulation purposes. Other video screens can display the complete page at full size.

Links to color makeup are still evolving. Typographic pagination is presently only available within "front end" systems or ad/page CAM terminals and interfaced to the color systems. Total integration is expected to take place, allowing page and multipage (signature) output on either films or plates.

## COLOR PAGE MAKEUP SYSTEMS

These are also known as *electronic pre-press systems* and, like *front end systems,* they attempt to perform all the steps from the original copy to the press plate in one system of integrated units. They consist of an electronic scanner, or interface with one; a digitizing tablet with cursor or tracer pen; computer storage, software, a high resolution video monitor for local and area correction and page makeup manipulation; and an output device to record the images of the completed pages or complete plate imposition on film or a printing plate. These systems input text, black-and-white and color illustrations, page layout and plate imposition instructions; perform the functions of color correc-

ELECTRONIC PRE-PRESS SYSTEM

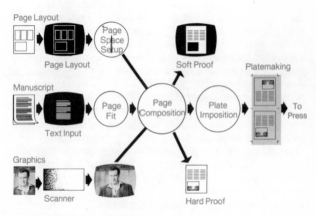

Page Layout

Page Layout · Page Space Setup · Soft Proof · Platemaking

Manuscript

Text Input · Page Fit · Page Composition · Plate Imposition · To Press

Graphics

Scanner · Hard Proof

tion, type composition, page makeup with all elements in correct position, soft proofing on VDT screens and signature imposition of all pages; and output the digital information with electronic laser dot generators onto film or high speed plates.

Typical systems in use are produced by *Scitex, Rudolph Hell, Crosfield,* and *Dainippon Screen* and others are in development. All systems are similar in function and accomplish the objective of eliminating most of the handwork and expensive materials conventionally used in the pre-press areas of the color reproduction process.

Scitex systems have the ability to interface with any electronic color scanner, while the other systems use dedicated scanners. All are being adapted to text output at acceptable resolutions. A limitation of these systems is the inability to produce hard proofs (proof on paper or proofing medium). All have video display terminals (VDT) which display soft proofs; one system outputs a continuous-tone hard color proof from digital information onto color photographic paper.

All systems are designed so that most functions can be done off-line thus eliminating bottlenecks and enhancing flexibility. Some systems have input stations for art directors and graphic designers to input page layouts; others interface with text, line illustrations and scanners. These systems are expensive and more productive than most printers need or can afford. Most of these systems are being installed in trade shops which makes the sophisticated services available to all printers.

### Flat-Field Scanners

Sometimes referred to as electronic cameras, flat-field scanners can eventually replace conventional cameras and film for many applications as they combine optical imaging with electronic image manipulation. In a flat-field scanner an original illustration is scanned by a light source, usually a laser; the information is transmitted to a computer which digitizes and manipulates it electronically; and it is output through another optical system to a display medium like paper or film. In this series of steps the image can be reproduced at any size in either or both directions (*anamorphic* enlargement); it can be slanted, outlined, with or without borders, reversed, either laterally or from positive to negative; its detail can be increased or sharpened by techniques known as *unsharp masking* and *edge enhancement;* its tone reproduction can be adjusted to suit variable printing conditions; and it can be reproduced as continuous-tone or halftone in a range of screen rulings and with special dot configurations like a double dot, chain dot, random grain, etc.

Typical systems are made by AM/ECRM, Klimsch, Hell, Scitex and Imagitex. All these are used for processing single color images. The AM/ECRM Autokon 8400, introduced in 1975, has been used extensively by newspapers for both line and halftone reproductions up to 100-line screen in sizes up to 11 x 14 inches. The Autokon 8500 was introduced in 1982 with larger output and 120-line screen halftone capability. Also introduced in 1982 were the Klimsch Planescan with large format and 150-line screen capability; Hell Chromacom scanner for text input with resolution up to 2500 lines per inch (equivalent to 250-line screen); Scitex Ray Star with resolution of 1444 lines per inch (144-line screen); and Imagitex which is a low cost image processing system intended for use with electronic publishing systems.

Flat-field scanners are also used for color; some with special arrays have been used in high speed electronic cameras and for TV video tape cameras. The EIKONIX color scanner uses a flat-field self-scan linear array processor as input which digitizes and stores it as colormetric data. Color correction, image sizing and positioning is done on a high resolution color monitor; and the output station has electronic dot generators and uses a He/Cd blue laser which allows the use of ordinary film.

## Computer-Aided Layout Systems

These are for companies wanting to increase productivity in pre-press areas but are not ready for the expensive sophisticated electronic pre-press systems. They are based on computer aided design/computer aided manufacturing (CAD/CAM) technology draftsmen and design engineers have been using to draw lines and geometric shapes with superior speed and precision to manual techniques. Use of these concepts by the printing industry to perform the image assembly (stripping) function of producing shaping masks, dropouts and undercuts for halftone and screen tint images is saving over 50% of the total image assembly time. Once the necessary mask films are made, all the craftsman has to do is lay-in (strip) the halftones and screen tints on the films, using the masks to crop and position the images for platemaking.

Typical systems are produced by three major high technology companies: Gerber Scientific Instrument Co., Dainippon Screen Manufacturing Co., and Shukosha. Common features of the modular systems produced by these companies are: *input* station with interactive image digitizer table; *output* unit with high speed plotter to produce photographic, scribed or masking film intermediates; and *accuracy* and *resolution* of ±0.004 inch (±0.102 mm) over a 48 inch (1220 mm) plotting area.

The systems are very cost effective; they relieve production in the film assembly department; they provide accurate films for 4-color process image assemblies; they offer new levels of mechanical accuracy for fully imposed film flats; and they are especially effective for complex magazine and catalog pages with multi-color halftone images, screen tint backgrounds and facing page crossover images.

## FUTURE

Computers and software have been responsible for many improvements in costs and productivity in graphic arts and they will continue to expand its horizons by extending these improvements to the pressroom and bindery. Now that printers realize they are a part of the vast information industry that dominates the US labor force and economy, computers and software will gradually usher printers into the use of information media other than paper and ink. These new media are electronic like Videotex, cable TV, electronic newspapers, paperless books, electronic shopping, electronic telephone directories, and even electronic publishing and ink jet printing. To prepare themselves for these media, a number of newspaper and magazine publishers already own cable TV stations.

# Platemaking

An important step in all printing processes is the making of the intermediate image carrier — plate or cylinder — which is used for printing on the press. As would be expected, each printing process uses a different kind of image carrier. It determines the characteristics of the image produced, the type of ink and press to be used, the number of impressions that can be printed, and the speed with which they are printed. The image carrier is the hub around which each printing process revolves.

## METHODS OF PRODUCING PRINTING IMAGE CARRIERS

Image carriers can be made in a number of ways depending on the printing process, length of run, type of press, etc.

**Manual** image carriers consist of hand-set composition, wood-cuts, linoleum blocks, copperplate or steel-die engravings, all produced manually, as was done for hundreds of years after the invention of movable type. These are seldom used now except for short runs and unusual effects. Manually made images are still used commercially in screen printing and manually drawn images on stone are used by artists to produce original or limited editions of lithographs.

**Mechanical** image carriers are produced mainly for relief printing. They fall into two categories: (1) hot-metal machine composition and (2) duplicate printing plates. In duplicate platemaking, each of the different kinds is arrived at by a different production method and with different materials.

Intaglio printing also uses mechanically made plates such as pantograph engravings and engravings made with geometric lathes. Pantograph engravings are used in steel-die engraving. Geometric lathes produce scrolls and other patterns used for stock and bond certificates and paper currency. Mechanically made gravure cylinders are also used for the printing of textiles, wrapping papers, wallpapers and plastics.

**Photomechanical** platemaking is the most important and universally used method of platemaking. It uses light-sensitive coatings on which images are produced photographically and processed according to the requirements of the printing method used *(see Photomechanics, next page)*. Photomechanics overcomes the limitations of manually and mechanically produced plates and is capable of reproducing photographs and other pictorial subjects.

**Electro-mechanical** equipment has been used to convert original images directly into relief printing plates. These were used primarily for low-cost picture reproduction for newspapers.

Electro-mechanical engraving machines are used extensively for making gravure cylinders *(see page 124).*

**Electrostatic** plates are popular in reprography (offset duplicating) where electrophotographic cameras convert original images or pasteups to lithographic plates used on copier/duplicators *(see page 32)*. Electrostatically produced plates are also used for imaging from pasteups and for laser platemaking for newspaper printing *(see page 121).*

## PHOTOMECHANICS

The light-sensitive coatings used in the photomechanical process change in physical properties after exposure to light. The exposed areas of the coating become insoluble in water or other solutions. The unexposed areas dissolve, leaving the exposed portion as an image, or a stencil to form an image.

Originally, natural organic substances such as asphalt and shellac and natural organic colloids like albumin and gum arabic were used as ingredients for photomechanical coatings. Chemists have introduced new materials such as polyvinyl alcohol, diazo compounds, photopolymers, etc. Until 1950, when diazo presensitized plates were introduced, practically all coatings used for photomechanical plates were colloids sensitized by bichromates which are becoming obsolete because of the possibility of problems with pollution and toxicity.

**Bichromated coatings** still in use are bichromated gelatin for gravure carbon tissue and collotype, and bichromated gum arabic for deep-etch and bimetal plates. The coatings are usually applied to metal plates in a *whirler* which spreads the coating over a whirling plate by centrifugal force. Use of bichromated colloids requires considerable skill and judgment. Sensitivity is affected by a number of factors such as temperature, relative humidity, pH (acidity) and coating thickness, which itself is affected by surface roughness, relative humidity, rate of application of coating, coating temperature and viscosity. The difficulty of controlling these factors has helped promote the use of presensitized and precoated plates for all processes.

**Diazo coatings** are used for presensitized and wipe-on aluminum lithographic plates. With wipe-on plates, the coating is wiped on with a sponge or applied with a roller coater. Plates may have either a relatively smooth or finely grained surface which has been pretreated with a silicate or anodized to accept the coating and to prevent a reaction with the metal. Diazo coatings are thin and are used for press runs under 100,000 impressions. Some prelacquered plates are capable of runs over

200,000 impressions. While most diazo coatings are used for negative plates, there are coatings for presensitized positive plates, deep-etch and bimetal plates. The main advantage of diazo coatings is that they are not affected much by changes in temperature and relative humidity. Temperatures above 125°F can cause scumming of plates. Storage life for presensitized plates is about a year.

**Photopolymer coatings** is a generic term for the use of synthetic resins for platemaking. They are usually very inert and abrasion resistant which allows press runs longer than those usually obtained with diazo coatings especially when baked.

Photopolymer plates are always supplied precoated. They are not only resistant to abrasion but also have low sensitivity to changes in temperature and relative humidity. They have long storage life before use, and good wear characteristics in printing. Some have good solvent resistance so they can be used in processes like flexography that use solvent inks.

### Plate Exposure

Two methods for plate exposure are in common use today: (1) *Vacuum frame* and (2) *Step and repeat*.

**Vacuum frame** Exposures on plates are made in a vacuum frame if all the negatives are stripped up on a single flat or if the same flat is to be exposed two or more times on a plate, in which case pin register devices are used to make sure that the exposures are made in the proper position. Sometimes two or more flats are exposed on the same plate. This is known as *surprinting* or *multiple burns*. This is done with flats consisting of negatives, but cannot be done with positives. When plates are made from positives, all elements must be combined on one flat before the exposure is made.

**Step and repeat** When more than four exposures are to be made on a plate from the same subject, it is usually more economical and accurate to use a step-and-repeat machine which is designed to produce multiple images of negatives or positives on a printing plate. It consists of a bed for mounting the plate which is usually held by vacuum during exposure; a chase for mounting the film for exposure; a means for traversing the chase accurately in two directions; and a high intensity lamp like pulsed Xenon or metal halide for exposure.

Some step-and-repeat machines have devices for moving the chase in both directions automatically using punched tape, punched cards, computer keyboard or program. Some are also equipped with film cassettes so that they operate completely automatically by rejecting one film after all the exposures with that film have been completed and picking up the next film for continuing the exposures on the plate. One machine uses a keyboard and CRT for input. Such automated machines are very useful in packaging and label printing where a number of exposures of different subjects are made on a plate. The automatic machines are also useful in book production where the negatives are programmed in advance for exposure in the proper position on the plate.

MISOMEX STEP AND REPEAT

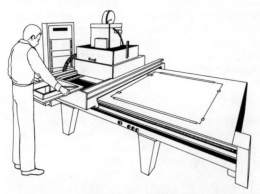

## LETTERPRESS AND FLEXOGRAPHIC PLATES

Plates used for letterpress printing can be *original, duplicate,* or *wraparound.* Original plates are usually photoengravings made on zinc, magnesium or copper of about 16 gauge (0.065″) in thickness. They are called *direct* plates if they are used for printing. Photopolymer plates are usually direct plates. Some are used to make molds for duplicate plates, such as mats for stereotypes. Duplicate plates are made from original engravings and can be plastic, rubber, stereotypes or electrotypes. Most direct and duplicate plates are made in small units or page size for assembly in a form or on the printing cylinder of the press. Flexography uses rubber duplicate plates and special photopolymer plates.

Wraparound plates as used for *dry offset* or *letterset* printing are made in one piece to be wrapped around the plate cylinder of a press. All copy is in proper position for printing. Setup or makeready time is substantially reduced. Plates are plastic or metal, ranging from 0.017″ to 0.030″ in thickness so they can be bent to fit into the cylinder clamps.

## Photoengraving

The oldest of the photomechanical processes, photoengraving pertains to the production of relief printing plates for letterpress. Photoengraved plates fall into two categories: *line* and *halftone*. In the U.S., line and coarse screen engravings are made on zinc and magnesium, and fine screen halftone plates are made on copper. In Europe, zinc is used for all types of engravings.

**Conventional etching** The plate is coated with a light-sensitive coating, exposed to a negative and processed. The exposed coating serves as a resist for protecting the image areas as the non-image areas are etched in acid baths. The main problem in conventional etching is to maintain the correct dot and line width at the proper etch depth which is accomplished by *scale compression* in the negative and *four-way powdering* in stages or *bites* on the engraving. Because conventional etching is time consuming and requires considerable skill and judgment, it has been replaced almost completely by powderless etching.

**Powderless etching** can be used for zinc, magnesium, and copper plates. Zinc and magnesium use the same process. Copper uses essentially the same principles, but the chemicals and mechanism are different. The plate is prepared as in the conventional process, but a special etching machine is used. Zinc and magnesium are etched in an emulsion of dilute nitric acid, a wetting agent and an oil. During etching, the wetting agent and oil attach to the surface of the metal, forming an etch-resistant coating on the sidewalls of the etched elements, thus preventing undercutting.

In copper etching, the etchant used is ferric chloride, in which certain organic chemicals are dissolved. During etching, the additive chemicals react with the dissolved metal, to form a gelatinous precipitate which adheres to the sides of the image elements and protects them from undercutting.

**Photopolymer plates** are usually precoated and can be used as original (or direct), pattern and wraparound plates. There are many in use today, of which DuPont *Dycril* is the oldest. At present the BASF Nyloprint plate, on a steel base and mounted on magnetic cylinders, is the most popular plate used in letterpress for magazine and commercial printing. Photopolymer plates used in newspaper printing are the W.R. Grace *Letterflex, Dynaflex,* Hercules *Merigraph* and *Napp* plates. Some of these plates have been adapted for use in flexography and on belt presses *(see page 130).*

## Duplicate Plates

Original photoengravings can be used directly for printing or to make molds from which duplicate plates are made for the actual printing. This is desirable for long runs and is necessary where the plates are made on flat metal and the printing plates need to be curved for mounting on the cylinders of rotary presses. Also the original and mold are always available in case printing plates are damaged. The four types of duplicate plates in use are *stereotypes, electrotypes, plastic* and *rubber* plates.

**Stereotypes** have been used almost exclusively for letterpress newspaper printing but they are gradually being replaced by photopolymer and lithographic plates. A matrix, or *mat* as it is called, is made from the original plate using a special papier-mâché and the printing plate is cast by pouring molten metal into the mold. Once the mat is made, duplicate plates can be made

FOUR STEPS IN MAKING A STEREO

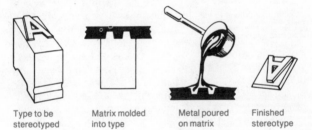

| Type to be stereotyped | Matrix molded into type | Metal poured on matrix | Finished stereotype |

in less than a minute at very reasonable cost. For long runs the plates can be nickel or chromium plated. Run length is not an important factor in newspaper printing. Presses are seldom run over two hours in which time about 100,000 newspapers are printed. If more papers are needed, more presses are used.

**Electrotypes** are used for quality letterpress commercial, book and magazine printing. An impression is made of the original engraving in hot plastic which is plated with silver to make it conductive, after which a thin shell of copper or nickel is plated by an electrolytic process. The shell is backed with molten metal and the face can be nickel, chromium or iron plated for long runs up to several million.

**Plastic and rubber plates** have the advantage of lightness in weight and low cost. They are made from molds similar to those used for electrotypes. Plastic plates are molded from thermoplastic vinyl resins and are used for some types of commercial printing. Rubber plates are molded from either natural or synthetic rubber or combinations of them, depending on the solvents used in the inks for printing. Rubber plates are used mainly in flexography for printing on rough surfaces such as envelopes, bags, tags, wrapping paper, corrugated boxes, milk cartons, as well as on extensible films for flexible packaging.

## LITHOGRAPHIC PLATES

Lithography is based on the principle that grease and water do not mix. On a lithographic plate the separation between the image and non-image areas is maintained chemically since they are essentially on the same plane; the image areas must be ink receptive and refuse water, and the non-image areas must be water receptive and refuse ink. In reality, ink and water do mix slightly. If they didn't, lithography would not be possible. If they mix too much, there are problems. The wider the difference maintained between the ink receptivity of the image areas and the water receptivity of the non-image areas, the better the plate will be, the easier it will run on the press, and consequently, the better the printing.

Ink receptivity is achieved with inherently oleophilic (oil-loving) resins or metals like copper or brass on the image areas. Water receptivity of the non-image areas is usually achieved by using metals like aluminum, chromium or stainless steel whose oxides are hydrophilic (water-loving). Water receptivity is maintained in platemaking and storage by using natural and synthetic gums. The most widely used is gum arabic.

Most lithographic plates use either grained or anodized aluminum as a base. An advantage of lithographic plates, besides simplicity and low cost, is the ease of making minor corrections on the press. If corrections are extensive, however, it is more economical to make a new plate. Tone values can be easily controlled with the use of the GATF Sensitivity Guide, Star Target, Dot Gain Scale, and QC Strip *(see page 143)*.

There are three types of lithographic plates: *surface, deep-etch* and *bimetal*.

### Surface Plates

Surface plates are those in which the light-sensitive coating becomes the ink-receptive image area on the plate. Most are made from negatives. There are two types of surface plates, *additive* and *subtractive*. On the additive plate the ink-receptive lacquer is added to the plate during processing. On the subtractive plate it is part of the precoating, and processing removes it from the non-printing areas. Such plates are also called prelacquered plates.

Until recently all surface plates were used for short or medium runs. For many years albumin plates dominated this field but they are now obsolete. Surface plates are presently either diazo presensitized (precoated) or wipe-on (in-plant coated) for short and medium runs, and prelacquered diazo presensitized and photopolymer plates for longer runs.

**Diazo** presensitized and wipe-on *additive* plates are easy to process. Most are made from negatives. Once exposed, they are treated with an emulsion developer which consists of a lacquer and gum-etch in acid solution. As the unexposed diazo is dissolved by the solution, the gum deposits on the non-printing areas insuring water receptivity, and lacquer deposits on the exposed images making them ink receptive. Once developed, the plate is rinsed with water and coated with a protective gum arabic solution. *Prelacquered* or *subtractive* plates are developed with a special solvent, washed and then gummed. On most surface plates made from positives the image must be stabilized during processing.

**Photopolymer plates** are both positive and negative. Each type can be processed either by hand or by special automatic processors. The finished plates are characterized by better abrasion resistance and longer press runs. Runs exceeding one million have been made from photopolymer plates baked in special ovens for 4–5 minutes at 500°–550°F (250°–275°C).

**Automatic processors** for platemaking are used almost as extensively as for photography. Each plate process or special plate has an automatic processor. These processors have been an important factor in the use of web offset by newspapers. Some processors combine exposure with the processing and gumming and several include coating and exposing as well.

AUTOMATIC PLATE PROCESSOR

## Deep-etch Plates

Deep-etch plates are made from positives. The coating is removed from the unexposed image areas which are coppered chemically and/or lacquered and inked so that they are ink receptive. The majority of deep-etch plates are made using grained aluminum plates and a bichromated gum arabic coating. Some deep-etch plates are presensitized and precoated and some are made on anodized aluminum. Procedures for making deep-etch plates are long, involved and require considerable skill. They are gradually becoming obsolete because of cost, heavy metal toxicity and water pollution problems.

## Bimetal Plates

Bimetal plates use materials similar to deep-etch. They consist of a metal base with one or more metals plated on it. There are two types of bimetal plates: (1) copper plated on stainless steel or aluminum and (2) chromium plated on copper or brass. (The copper can be plated on a third metal which becomes the base, as in trimetal plates.) Type I plates are made from negatives; Type II are made from positives. Bimetal plates are the most rugged and also the most expensive of lithographic plates, but they are capable of runs in the millions. The increase in cost is not significant when they are used on long runs. Some of the copper-plated plates are presensitized, although most bimetal plates are presently in-plant coated.

Bimetal plates are easiest to run on the press because they are almost indestructible. Should anything happen to the plate on press (the copper may refuse to take ink or the non-printing area may scum) a single acid treatment restores the plate to its original condition. With other types of plates, treatments used on press to restore ink-receptive areas often are injurious to water-receptive areas and vice versa. Like deep-etch, bimetal plates are being replaced by long run photopolymer plates because of cost, toxicity and water pollution problems.

## Waterless Plates

*Waterless lithography,* also called *driography,* is a planographic process like lithography but it prints without water. The process eliminates all of the disadvantages caused by the need for an ink-water balance in lithography but retains all its advantages of low plate costs, ease of makeready, high speed, and good print quality plus the advantages of letterpress in ease of printing and low waste.

Waterless plates generally consist of ink on aluminum for the printing areas and a silicone rubber for the non-image areas.

Silicone rubber has a very low surface energy and thus has the property of not wanting to be wet by anything, especially ink. However, under the pressure and heat of printing, ordinary litho ink has a tendency to smear over the silicone and cause scumming or *toning*.

3M, a pioneer in driography, has stopped manufacturing these plates because of their unreliability and high cost. *TORAY* of Japan has produced a system using a special printing ink and waterless plates made from positives in which the silicone rubber is cured by exposure. Runs of over 80,000 have been made. The plates have not been popular in the U.S. because most plants prefer plates made from negatives. A negative plate process is in development.

## Laser Platemaking

Lasers are high energy concentrated light sources which are used for scanning and recording images at high speed. Several platemaking systems have been developed in which helium-neon (He/Ne) lasers are used to scan a pasteup, and this information is processed to expose a plate with an Argon-Ion laser. Because the laser can be controlled by electronic impulses, it can be operated by digital signals from a computer, thus enabling satellite and facsimile transmission of plate images to remote printing locations.

Laser platemaking systems are presently being used by newspapers, book and specialty printers. An obstacle to more extensive use has been the slow speed and limited spectral sensitivity of conventional lithographic plates which necessitates the use of expensive, high energy lasers like Argon-Ion. With the availability of satisfactory high-speed plates, laser platemaking could become very cost effective because economical, low-energy, high reliability lasers like He/Cd could be used.

## High-Speed Plates

In addition to laser platemaking the methods of automated stripping described on page 100 would be much more practical and most effective if printing plates were available with sufficient speed for exposure by projection. Some 24-sheet posters are still made by projection, but these use conventional plates and very high intensity light sources like 150 amp arc lights for enlarging the images from fine screen halftone negatives. The newer projection systems for book printing are designed to use the illumination level common in cameras, so plates with the speed of lithtype films are required. Ordinary diazo and photopolymer presensitized plates have exposure speeds

100–1000 times slower than lithfilms. Electrostatic processes show promise but most (except KC) lack resolution for quality printing.

**Electrostatic plates** are based on the principles of the Xerox copier. There are two types: *plain paper* and *electrofax*. A photoconducter is sensitized to light by charging with a corona discharge, and on exposure the charge is dissipated in the areas struck by light. The charge remaining on the unexposed areas is made visible by applying a dry or liquid toner with an opposite charge. In the plain paper type, exemplified by Xerox, the photoconductor is selenium, and the toned image is transferred to plain paper or other substrate. In the electrofax process the photoconductor is zinc oxide in an organic binder with high resistivity which is coated on paper or other substrate, and the toned image either is fixed on the substrate or it is transferred to another substrate. Organic photoconductors are also used as well as cadmium sulfide.

Xerox type plates are made mostly for short runs in reprography (duplicating). Electrofax plates are used for both reprography and high speed laser imaging. The plates for laser imaging are coated on electrograined anodized aluminum either with zinc oxide and binder or an organic photoconductor. For use in printing, zinc oxide coated plates are treated and run on the press with a solution containing ferrocyanide which renders the non-printing areas water-receptive. With organic photoconductor plates, the coating must be removed in the non-printing areas, and these are treated with etch and gum to make them water-receptive. In the chemical removal process the images become slightly ragged which does not affect their use for newspaper printing. The Chemco Newsplate is an example of a zinc oxide coated plate. Examples of organic photoconductor plates are Hoechst-Kalle *Elfasol,* Howson-Algraphy *Electrolith* and Polychrome *OPC-VI.*

**Transfer plates** There are several electrostatic platemaking processes primarily for newspaper printing which produce a toned image of a page pasteup on a photoconductor surface and then transfer the toner to a lithographic plate which is fused, etched and gummed before printing on a press. The 3M *Pyrofax* process transfers the image to an intermediate rubber blanket which in turn transfers it to the grained metal printing plate. The Agfa-Gevaert *ElectroPlater* transfers the image directly to an aluminum plate by electrophoresis. Both systems produce plates capable of runs in excess of 120,000.

*KC-plates* are also transfer plates and are the most promising of the new thin film electrophotographic materials for use as projection and laser exposed plates. They have exposure speed equivalent to lithfilms and due to their high resolution are capable of good copy-dot quality for the reproduction of pasteups consisting of line and halftone copy. They can be exposed by He/Cd lasers, and are used in the KC-Color Proofer.

## GRAVURE PLATE AND CYLINDER MAKING

In **conventional** gravure, the image is transferred to the copper cylinder by the use of a sensitized gelatin transfer medium known as *carbon tissue.* The carbon tissue is first exposed in contact with an overall gravure screen. (The screen serves a purely mechanical purpose, and, unlike other processes, has nothing to do with producing the tones of the picture. It merely provides the partitions or walls of the cells etched into the cylinder to form a surface of uniform height for the doctor blade to ride on.) Then the continuous-tone positives are exposed in contact with the carbon tissue.

In the light tones of the positives, where light passes through freely, the gelatin on the carbon tissue becomes proportionately harder than where the light exposure is restrained. The carbon tissue thus has areas of varying hardness due to varying exposure to light. The carbon tissue is positioned on the copper plate or cylinder with precision machines. After removal of a paper backing, the tissue is developed in a tank of hot water, leaving gelatin of varying thickness in the square dot areas between the hardened screen lines. The etching is done in stages using solutions of ferric chloride at varying density (Baumé) levels. Photographic resists are being developed to replace the carbon tissue. They are more stable, easier to use and can be stored for a longer period of time. Conventional gravure is used for high quality black-and-white and color illustrations but mainly for short runs because of doctor blade wear of the shallow highlight dots.

THREE TYPES OF GRAVURE

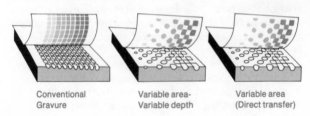

Conventional Gravure

Variable area-
Variable depth

Variable area
(Direct transfer)

The **variable area-variable depth** process for long run periodical printing differs from the conventional gravure process just described in that the *size* of the cells as well as the *depth* varies to produce more durable tones in publication printing. The highlight cells (lighter areas) are smaller but deeper. In this process continuous-tone positives and resists are used as in conventional gravure but instead of the overall screen, a special halftone positive is used.

In the **direct transfer** or *variable area* method an acid resistant light-sensitive coating is first applied to the copper. The screened positive is wrapped around the cylinder and exposed directly to it by a strong light source through a narrow slit as the cylinder turns. The cylinder is then developed, and the coating which has not been exposed by light is removed. The cylinder is etched producing image elements which vary in area but not in depth, so the number of tones is limited. This method is used widely in packaging and textile printing.

**Other methods** A major problem in gravure cylinder production has been the unpredictability of tone values due to variations in the etching process. A number of attempts are being made to correct this. One approach is to use *controlled etching* such as in the Acigraf and Crosfield processes and *powderless etching* as in photoengraving. Another is the method of *electromechanical engraving*, such as the Helioklischograph. In this equipment, positives or negatives of the copy made on a special opaque white plastic are scanned as the cylinder is being engraved electromechanically by special diamond styli. Research is being done on the use of *electron-beam* and *laser etching* of the copper cylinder which are considerably faster than electromechanical engraving. The *Lasergravure* process by Crosfield uses a plastic-coated copperplated cylinder in which helical grooves with variable depths and cross bridges are etched with a 100W $CO_2$ laser driven by a scanner or other front end system.

A process which is making gravure competitive and cost effective in runs as low as 100,000 is *offset-gravure conversion* in which offset positives are converted for gravure use with conventional etching or on Helioklischographs. The use of offset positives simplifies color separation, correction and pre-press proofing for gravure.

Gravure cylinders are chromium plated for long runs. On very long runs the chromium is worn off by friction of the doctor blade over the cylinder. In such cases the cylinder is removed, rechromed, and replaced in the press for continuing the run.

## SCREEN PRINTING

There are many methods of making screens for screen printing. As previously mentioned, the screen consists of a porous material, and the printed image is produced by blocking unwanted holes or *pores* of the screen.

Early screens were made manually by painting the image on silk mounted on a wooden frame. Masking materials were used to block out unwanted areas. Today, both hand-cut stencils and photomechanical means are used. In the photomechanical method the screen is coated with a light-sensitive emulsion; exposure is made through a screened film positive placed in contact with the screen and the coating in the unexposed areas is developed to form the image through which the ink flows to the substrate. The exposed areas form a hardened stencil which prevents the penetration of ink in these areas.

**Rotary screens** are made by plating a metal cylinder electrolytically on a steel cylinder, removing the metal cylinder after plating, applying a photo-sensitive coating to the cylinder, exposing it through a positive and a screen, and etching out the image areas to form pores in the cylinder. On rotary screen presses the ink is pumped into the cylinder, and the squeegee which is inside the cylinder controls the flow of ink to the substrate.

## PLATES FOR REPROGRAPHY

There are some unconventional plates used in reprography (duplicating) that have speeds on the order of lithfilms, but these are generally short run and have some quality limitations. They are *photographic, diffusion transfer, electrostatic* and *direct image* plates.

**Photographic plates** using chemically tanned silver halide emulsions for printing are made in two types. One is the *3M camera plate* system in which the plate is on a plastic base and is made directly in a camera, processed and mounted on the press. It is capable of runs up to 10,000. The other is the Kodak *Verilith* plate used successfully in the Itek Platemaster, A-M Photo-Direct and A.B. Dick Photomat duplicating systems. It consists of a paper base coated with two photographic emulsions and a third coating containing photographic developer. During exposure and processing, a plate is produced in which the unexposed or image areas of the copy are tanned and become ink-receptive, while the exposed non-image areas remain water-receptive. The plate has a critical ink-water balance and short range of tone reproduction, but is capable of runs of 5,000–10,000.

**Diffusion transfer plates** use materials similar to those described on page 78 for making screened prints. Most common materials for plates are Kodak *PMT* and Agfa-Gevaert *CopyRapid*. A negative of the image is produced on an intermediate surface, and the final positive image is transferred by diffusion to a specially coated receiver material. Such materials are used to produce direct screen separations and printing plates as well as screened prints. Some quality is sacrificed in the transfer, but plates have been produced capable of runs up to 50,000.

**Electrostatic plates** are used in reprography on offset duplicators and copier/duplicators *(see page 32)*. Most plates are of the electrofax type *(see page 122)*.

**Direct image plates** can be prepared by typing, drawing or lettering directly onto a paper or thin metal master using special ribbons, pencils, crayons and inks. The old lithographic stones are examples of direct image plates. Artists still draw on stone. Although inexpensive and easy to make, other direct image plates are limited in quality and are used only for short runs.

# Printing

Each printing process has distinguishing quality and appearance characteristics. The differences between the final printed images are not as noticeable as they were years ago. Lithography, letterpress and gravure are all capable of reproducing the same art and copy with equally satisfactory results. There are still some distinguishing characteristics, but these are minor. Letterpress is distinguished by sharp, crisp printing, but grainy images and sharp breaks in gradient tints and vignettes. Lithography is characterized by soft, smooth transitions of color and tones. Gravure has a long tone scale and strong, saturated colors. In most cases, however, factors such as economics, availability of equipment, and speed of delivery are the main considerations in selecting a printing process, rather than the intrinsic quality or appearance of the image.

The production machines of the Graphic Arts industry are the printing presses. They are mass production devices designed to handle the needs of a mass production society. There are many different kinds, but they all have similar basic features.

In general, a printing press must provide for: secure and precise mounting of the image carrier (and, in lithography, a blanket); accurate positioning of the paper during printing; conveying the paper through the printing units to the delivery; storing and applying ink (and, in lithography, a dampening solution) to the plate; accurately setting printing pressures for transfer of the inked image to the paper; and means for feeding blank, or partially-printed paper and for delivering printed paper.

Presses are either sheet-fed or roll- (web-) fed. Much commercial work is printed on *sheet-fed* presses. Magazines, newspapers, books and long run commercial work are printed on web-fed presses. Presses may be single color or multicolor. Usually each color on a multicolor press requires a separate complete printing unit consisting of inking, plate and impression mechanisms. A two-color press would have two such units, a four-color press would have four, etc. Some presses share a common impression mechanism among two or more printing units and are known as *common impression cylinder (CIC)* presses. Packaging and other special purpose equipment may have combinations of lithographic, letterpress and gravure units. A *perfecting* press is one which prints both sides of the paper in one pass through the press. All web and many sheet-fed presses are designed to perfect.

## LETTERPRESS

There are three basic letterpress presses: *platen, flat-bed cylinder,* and *rotary*. In addition there is the *belt press* for continuous in-line printing.

THREE TYPES OF LETTERPRESS

| Platen | Flat-bed Cylinder | Rotary |

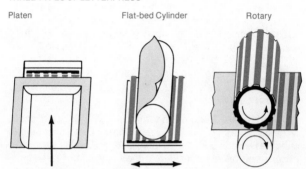

**Platen Press** carries both the paper and the type form on flat surfaces. Known as the *platen* and the *bed,* these two surfaces open and close like the jaws of a clamshell. As the jaws of the press open, the type form on the bed is inked and a sheet of paper is fed to the platen. As the jaws close, the sheet is printed. When they open again, the printed sheet is delivered and a new sheet is fed to the platen.

On most platen presses the amount of impression or *squeeze* is controlled by an impression lever which makes the press extremely versatile. It is used for short-run job printing such as announcements, invitations, name cards, stationery, etc. Larger platen presses are used for embossing, die-cutting and scoring.

**Flat-bed Cylinder Press** has a moving flat bed which holds the form while a fixed rotating impression cylinder provides the pressure. The paper, held securely to the cylinder by a set of *grippers,* is rolled over the form as the bed passes under the cylinder. As the bed returns to its original position, the cylinder is raised, the form re-inked, and the printed sheet delivered.

On *vertical presses* where the bed is in a vertical position both form and cylinder move up and down in a reciprocating motion, thus making only one revolution for every printed impression, vs. two for the flat-bed press. With the exception of the vertical press, the flat-bed cylinder press has become obsolete. It has not been manufactured in the U.S. for many years.

**Rotary Press** is the fastest and most efficient of the three types of letterpress machines and has been used mainly for long runs. Some large sheet-fed rotaries are still used for packaging, but, due to the declining market for letterpress, this press, like the flat-bed cylinder press, is no longer manufactured in the U.S.

On rotary presses both the impression and printing surfaces are cylindrical: the plate cylinder holds the plates, the impression cylinder provides the pressure, and the sheet is printed with *each* revolution of the impression cylinder. Plates for rotary presses must be curved to the circumference of the plate cylinder, and electros and stereos are mostly used. Special lockup devices are used to hold curved plates on the cylinder. Steel backed polymer plates and magnetic cylinders are recent advances in plate mounting.

**Web-fed Rotary Press** prints a continuous roll or *web* of paper on both sides as it passes through the press. One side is printed and dried first, as opposed to the blanket-to-blanket web offset press which prints both sides of the paper at the same time. These presses are used for all types of printing, from newspapers to fine color work in magazines and catalogs.

In newspaper presses, multiple printing couples (term used to describe a paired impression and plate cylinder) can be used, each couple perfecting a single web, and the multiple webs are assembled and folded in a single folder.

Most multicolor web-fed rotaries are of the common impression cylinder type. Special inks and dryers are used. The presses are operated at speeds over 1500 feet per minute. The paper is fed with automatic splicing from one roll to another. The printed web is either sheeted or folded into signatures at the delivery end of the press.

**Belt Press** is an automated in-line press which prints, collates, and binds a complete book in one pass through the press. It has two belts on which the plates for all the pages in the book are mounted. In printing, a roll of paper is fed in contact with the first belt which prints all the pages for one side, after which the ink is dried, the paper turned over and run in contact with the second belt to print the other side. The paper is then dried, slit into ribbons, cut into four-page signatures and collated as complete books at the rate of 1200 feet per minute or 250 240-page books a minute. The collated books can be fed on a conveyor into an automatic perfect binder, where the covers are attached and the completed books are delivered ready for shipment.

**Flexographic Presses** are also web-fed machines. There are three types: (1) *Stack type* in which two or three printing units are placed vertically in stacks. A press may consist of two or three stacks, with unwind, rewind, sheeter or cutter and creaser; (2) *Central impression cylinder* which is like the common impression rotary letterpress and is used extensively for printing flexible films; (3) *In-line* which is similar to a unit type rotary press.

Flexography is an inexpensive and simple printing process used extensively for decorating and packaging printing. It uses rubber plates and water- or solvent-based inks in simple two-roller inking systems. Quality has not been a prime objective, but recently good quality printing, including up to 150-line halftones, has been achieved on paper and flexible films by using special photopolymer plates, reverse angle doctor blades, and ceramic inking rollers in central impression cylinder presses. These developments have opened up new markets for flexography, such as book, newspaper and heat transfer printing.

Most paperback books are printed by flexography using rubber plates and solvent inks. Shorter runs of heat transfer printing for polyester fabrics are also printed by flexography *(see page 138)*. The most promising new market for flexography is newspaper printing, where the use of water-base inks not only minimizes dependency on oil-base solvents but eliminates the annoying smudging of newspaper printing.

## Makeready

One of the problems of letterpress printing is the variable pressure exerted by different size image elements in printing. The same amount of pressure, or *squeeze,* needed for ink transfer exerts greater pressure per unit area on small highlight dots than on larger shadow dots. Expensive makeready is needed to even out the impression so that highlights print correctly and do not puncture the paper. Precision electros, wraparound plates and pre-makeready systems help reduce makeready cost. In flexography, makeready is not critical because the resilient plate distorts and compresses but the distortion can limit the quality of the screened image and the register in printing.

## OFFSET LITHOGRAPHY

The offset press is responsible for the following important advantages in lithography: (1) the rubber printing surface conforms to irregular printing surfaces, resulting in the need for less pressure, improved print quality, and halftones of good quality on rough surfaced papers; (2) paper does not contact the metal plate, increasing plate life and reducing abrasive wear; (3) the image on the plate is straight reading rather than reverse reading; (4) less ink is required for equal coverage, drying is speeded up, and smudging and set-off are reduced.

### The Offset Press

All offset presses make one impression with *each* revolution of the cylinders. Offset presses have three printing cylinders (plate, blanket and impression) as well as inking and dampening systems *(see illustration, page 29)*. As the plate which is clamped to the plate cylinder rotates, it comes in contact with the *dampening* rollers first, then the *inking* rollers. The dampeners wet the plate so the non-printing area will repel ink. The inked image is then transferred to the rubber blanket, and paper is printed as it passes between the blanket and impression cylinders.

OFFSET PRESS

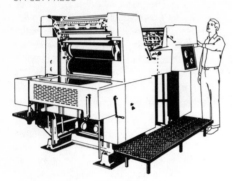

Makeready is minimal; the wraparound plates can be shifted slightly for proper register. The resilient rubber blanket compensates for the varying thicknesses and textures of paper stocks, largely eliminating a source of considerable trouble in other printing processes. A wide range of papers can be used. Halftones can be printed with text and solids on both rough and smooth surface papers.

**Sheet-fed Presses** have been made in sizes up to 55″ x 78″. The larger presses are used mainly for printing specialties like greeting cards, gift wrappings, posters, and packaging. Most commercial sheet-fed printing is on 25″ x 38″ to 38″ x 50″ presses. They can print at speeds up to 11,000 impressions per hour and are made as single or multicolor presses up to 6 units. Sheet-fed printing has the advantages that (1) a large number of sheet or format sizes can be printed on the same press, and (2) waste sheets can be used during makeready, so good paper is not spoiled while getting position or color up for running.

**Sheet-fed Perfecting Presses** are made in many sizes. Some of these presses are single color utilizing the *blanket-to-blanket* principle. Most of the newer presses are *convertible*. They are made in units from two to six colors. A two-unit convertible press prints either two colors on one side or one color on two sides, with minimum changeover time. The sheet is turned between printing units. One six-unit model can be made to print six colors on one side; five colors on one side, one color on the other side; four and two; three and three. Not all perfecting presses have this versatility; some have fixed configurations.

**Letterset (Dry Offset)** uses a blanket for transferring the image from plate to paper but unlike conventional offset, it uses a relief wraparound plate and requires no dampening system, thereby eliminating all water problems. Standard offset presses must be modified slightly for letterset because the plates are usually thicker. Other advantages of letterset are quicker setting of inks, with more consistent color throughout the run, and somewhat higher ink gloss.

**Web Offset** Much of the growth in the lithographic industry in recent years can be attributed to web offset which is used to produce newspapers, magazines, business forms, computer letters, mail order catalogs, gift wrappings, books, encyclopedias, and a variety of commercial printing. The 38″ web offset press has almost completely displaced large sheet-fed presses 60″ and larger for books, periodicals and commercial printing. Recently the half-size, or 8-page web, (17″ – 31″ width) has made serious inroads on the 25″ x 38″ to 38″ x 50″ sheet-fed market. The latest innovations in web offset are the 32-page presses in common impression and in-line design which make web offset competitive with gravure in long run printing.

Speed is the main advantage of web offset. Speeds of 1000 feet per minute are common, and special presses have been designed for speeds up to 1800 feet per minute and faster. Most web offset presses have in-line folders where various combinations of folds convert the web into folded signatures. Other in-line operations that can be performed on-press include paste binding, perforating, numbering, rotary sheeting and slitting. All of these make web offset very flexible, and all are done while presses are running at high speeds, up to four times faster than sheet-fed presses.

The main disadvantage of web offset (and web letterpress) is that they have a fixed cut-off (i.e., all sheets cut off at the same length). A major advantage of rotogravure is that cylinders with different diameters can be readily interchanged on the press allowing for different cut-offs or image sizes. Some variable cut-off presses for web offset have been designed, but these are mainly for packaging or printing one side. Attempts at variable cut-off blanket-to-blanket presses have been very cumbersome, expensive and impractical.

BLANKET-TO-BLANKET PRINTING UNIT

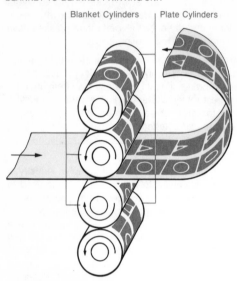

Blanket Cylinders | Plate Cylinders

There are three types of web offset presses:

(1) The **blanket-to-blanket press** has no impression cylinders. The blanket cylinder of one unit acts as the impression cylinder for the other, and vice versa. Each printing unit has two plate and two blanket cylinders. The paper is printed on *both* sides at the same time as it passes between the two blanket cylinders.

(2) The **in-line open press** is similar to a sheet-fed offset press, except that the cylinder gap is very narrow. Grippers and transfer cylinders are eliminated. Each unit prints one color on one side; additional units are required for additional colors. To print the reverse side, the web is turned over between printing units by means of *turning bars*, which expose the unprinted side of the web to the remaining printing units. This type of press is used extensively for printing business forms.

(3) The drum or **common impression cylinder (CIC) press** has all the blanket cylinders grouped around a large common impression cylinder. Two to five colors are printed in rapid succession on one side, after which the web is dried, turned, and the reverse side is printed in the same manner. It is possible to

print both sides on the same printing unit by a process known as *double ending*. A web one-half the width of the drum is printed, dried, turned over, and brought back through the other half of the drum for printing the reverse side.

**Dampening Systems** The conventional dampening system on offset presses transfers the dampening solution directly to the plate. In the Dahlgren type of direct-feed dampening system, the fountain solution containing up to 25% alcohol is metered to the plate through the inking system, or can be applied directly to the plate as in other systems. In general, this type of dampening system uses less water and reduces paper waste at start-up of the press. Because of the cost of isopropyl alcohol and potential health hazards in its use, a number of new fountain solutions have been developed to reduce or replace the alcohol in this type of dampening system.

**Inking Systems** are designed to transport ink to the printing plate. All systems use composition rollers. Some have plastic coated rollers and others have copper-plated steel rollers to prevent stripping of ink on the distributors. Some inking systems especially on web presses are water cooled. Two of the reasons for the large number of rollers in inking systems have been (1) the need to work the ink so that it flows properly and (2) with old albumin and zinc plates which required a lot of water for dampening, a large roller surface area was needed to evaporate the water from the ink to keep it from water-logging and emulsifying. With newer plates and dampening systems, less water is needed for printing. New inking systems have been proposed which have one large transfer roller for inking and either a doctor blade or a small roller for metering the ink. In these systems a new charge of ink is used for each revolution so that printing problems of ghosts, streaks and ink starvation are eliminated or, at least, minimized.

### Screenless Printing

Screenless Printing is a means of printing continuous-tone images from lithographic plates. Best results have been obtained with special printing plates and positive films. The plates are run conventionally on the press with regular inks and dampening solutions. Screenless printing has two main advantages: (1) Moiré patterns are eliminated, (2) Colors are purer and more saturated because most of the paper is covered with a random grain ink pattern and colors are not grayed or dirtied as they are in halftone printing because of the absorption of light in the paper between the dots.

More printing is not done by screenless lithography because of inconsistency of plate coatings. The tone reproduction of plate coatings depends on the roughness of the plate surface and the thickness of the coating, neither of which can be accurately controlled in manufacture. Manufacturers are working on improving plate consistency. Another approach to screenless printing is the use of extremely fine random grain screen images of the order of 500–600 lines per inch using special screens. Results are promising. Still another approach may be the production of random screen images on electronic scanners.

## GRAVURE

**Rotogravure** printing units consist of a printing cylinder, an impression cylinder, and an inking system. Ink is applied to the printing cylinder by an ink roll or spray, and the excess is removed by a doctor blade and returned to the ink fountain. The impression cylinder is covered with a rubber composition that presses the paper into contact with the ink in the tiny cells of the printing surface. Gravure inks are volatile and dry almost instantly. Hot air dryers are used between printing units to speed up drying. Therefore, in color printing each succeeding color is printed on a *dry color*, rather than on one which is still wet as in letterpress and offset. For color printing, presses use photoelectric cells for automatic register control. Cylinders are chromium plated for press runs of a million or more. When the chromium starts to wear, it is stripped off and the cylinder rechromed.

Gravure is used in packaging for quality color printing on transparent and flexible films (any cut-off length is possible by changing the size of the printing cylinder); also, for printing cartons, including die-cutting and embossing which can be done in-line on the press. Most long run magazines and mail order catalogs are printed by gravure. Among the specialties printed by gravure are vinyl floor coverings, upholstery and other textile materials, pressure-sensitive wall coverings, plastic laminates, imitation wood grains, tax and postage stamps and long run heat transfer patterns.

The largest publication gravure presses can print a web 106″ wide; for printing floor coverings, multicolor gravure presses can print webs up to 150″ wide. Presses used for packaging materials usually have webs from 40″ to 60″ wide with up to eight printing units. While speeds of 2000 feet per minute and more are used in publication and catalog printing, average production speeds of up to 800 feet per minute are more realistic on other types of work. One disadvantage of gravure for publication printing

GRAVURE PRESS

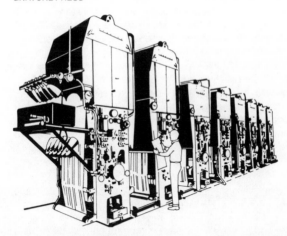

has been the inability to change pages on the cylinder. Wraparound printing cylinder segments have been introduced which give gravure this added capability.

**Sheet-fed Gravure** presses operate on the same rotary principle as rotogravure. The preparatory work is identical. The image is etched flat on a flexible sheet of copper which is then clamped around the plate cylinder of the press. Sheet-fed gravure is primarily used for short runs and press proofing. Because of the high quality and plate-making expense, it is used for art and photographic reproductions and prestige printing such as annual reports. In packaging, sheet-fed gravure presses are used for printing new packages for market testing.

**Offset Gravure** has been used for printing wood grains and in packaging. In this application, a converted flexographic press is used. The anilox roller is replaced by a gravure cylinder and doctor blade for printing the image and the plate cylinder of the flexographic press is covered with a solid rubber plate.

## SCREEN PRINTING

Some screen printing is done by hand with very simple equipment consisting of a table, screen frame and squeegee. Most commercial screen printing, however, is done on power-operated presses. There are both roll-fed and sheet-fed presses, with hot air dryers, which run at speeds up to 400 feet per minute or over 5,000 impressions per hour.

There are two types of power-operated presses. One type uses flat screens which require an intermittent motion as each screen is printed. Butts and overlaps require close register, which limits running speed. The latest type uses rotary screens with the squeegee mounted inside the cylinder and the ink pumped in automatically. These presses are continuous running, fast, and print continuous patterns with little difficulty.

The amount of ink applied by screen printing is far greater than in letterpress, lithography, or gravure which accounts for some of the unusual effects in screen printing. Because of the heavy ink film, the sheets must be racked separately until dry, or passed through a heated tunnel or drier before they can be stacked safely without smudging or set-off. UV curing ink has simplified drying and is helping to promote greater use of screen printing.

Screen printing prints on almost any surface, and both line and halftone work can be printed. It is used for art prints, posters, decalcomania transfers, greeting cards, menus, program covers and wallpaper. Screen printing is important in the printing of textiles such as tablecloths, shower curtains and draperies. It is particularly adapted to the printing of leather, metal, glass, wood, ceramic materials and plastics, both flat and in finished molded form. By printing an adhesive size and then dusting with cotton, silk, or rayon flock, the finished design can be made to appear like felt or suede leather. It is also used for printing integrated circuits for electronics.

Screen printing has distinct advantages for short runs because of the simplicity of equipment needed. For longer runs, the advantage is soon lost since other printing methods are so much faster and more economical. However, for most of the applications listed, screen printing is the only practical process.

## HEAT TRANSFER PRINTING

This process is used for producing printed products in which images are printed on paper with special inks and are then transferred to the desired substrate by heat and pressure. The process was developed for producing images and/or patterns on polyester fabrics. The inks contain special sublimable dyes which transfer to the polyester materials under the heat and pressure used. The process is an economical way of preparing images for use on expensive materials like polyester fabrics. The printing processes used most extensively for heat transfer printing are gravure for long runs, flexography for shorter runs, screen printing for very short runs, and offset lithography for sizable runs on sheet or piece goods.

## ELECTRONIC AND INK JET PRINTING

These are plateless printing processes in which the data representing the images are in digital form in computer storage, and the image must be created each time it is reproduced; so to print 1000 copies of a subject, the image must be composed from digital information in the computer 1000 times. This distinguishes electronic and ink jet printing from conventional printing processes which use plates or cylinders. In these processes the image is produced once on the plate which is printed on a press to produce the required number of copies. The chances of all the copies looking alike are much greater in conventional plate printing than in electronic or ink jet printing where the image must be created each time it is reproduced. These processes, therefore, are more practical for printing variable information like addresses, coding, computer letters, etc.

**Electronic printing**, like a plain paper copier, prints from a photoconductor drum. A laser beam directed by computer commands produces a pattern of latent charged images on the drum which are developed by toner and transferred to plain paper. The images can be quickly erased and repeated or changed. Such an all-electronic printing process can go directly from the computer or memory to the printed sheet without process photography, stripping and platemaking. Examples of such printers are Xerox 9700, IBM 3800, and Honeywell Page Printing System. These are presently used to produce forms, reports, bills, etc. Interfacing these printers with image digitizers like ECRM Autokon and typesetters will produce completely integrated publishing systems which will be used for short run publishing of illustrated books, pamphlets, reports and manuals.

**Ink Jet printing** is a means of pressureless printing which creates images with jets of colored fluid similar to fountain pen ink. The ink is sprayed through a nozzle under pressure, broken up into uniform droplets, charged electrically and deflected by a computer or other image generating device.

There are two types of ink jet printers. In one type, a single nozzle activated by a computer oscillates back and forth over a sheet much as an electron beam produces an image on a TV screen. This is the principle of AB Dick *Videojet* system which produces non-contact printing of more than 1300 characters per second and is used for coding and addressing materials while they are being printed. The other type of ink jet printer uses a bank of nozzles each of which is digitally controlled by a computer program. As many as 200 to 300 jets per inch are used that can image up to 50,000 characters per second or 70,000 news-paper lines of type per minute. This is the principle of the Mead *Digit* system.

## REPROGRAPHY

As described on page 31, reprography consists of all the processes used for making copies of original documents. Copiers are the main equipment of reprography, but the offset duplicator is also an important piece of reprographic equipment which is described in greater detail here. As *in-plant* and *quick* printing increase, reprography becomes more competitive with other processes for some graphic arts markets.

**Offset Duplicator** is a small offset lithographic press which is used for fast, good quality reproduction of copies in sizes from 3″ x 5″ up to 14″ x 20″. Offset duplicators are ideal for low cost printing of business forms, letterheads, labels, bulletins, postcards, envelopes, folders, reports, and sales literature. Single-color jobs predominate, but a large amount of multicolor work is done. There are over 200,000 offset duplicators in business, industrial, financial, educational, governmental and commercial printing plants.

OFFSET DUPLICATOR

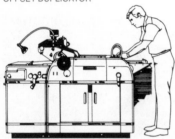

Machines are made for simplified operation and convenience. The offset duplicator is a compact, heavy-duty, reliable, high production machine with many built-in features for fast job changeovers and minimum makeready. They can print on sheet stock from lightweight onionskin up to cardboard at speeds up to 9,000 impressions per hour (iph). Web duplicators are more limited in use, but are capable of speeds up to 25,000 iph.

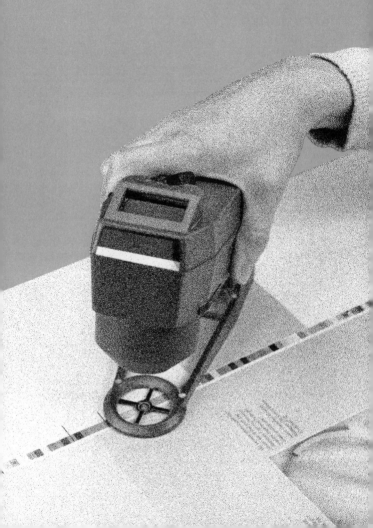

Printing is a manufacturing process. Since machinery that wears, and variable products like paper, inks, press blankets, fountain solutions, plates, films, etc. are used in the process, every effort must be made to control them. The system by which the printed product is measured, examined and controlled is *quality control.* Successful quality control depends on four functions: (1) Specifications and control of raw materials, (2) Control of the printing process, (3) Standards and tolerances of acceptability and (4) Inspection of the final product.

## RAW MATERIALS

The printing processes use many raw materials. Unless a printer is willing to install extensive and expensive laboratory testing facilities, he should develop honest working relationships with his suppliers and their technical representatives, and establish realistic specifications for the raw materials he uses. Important material properties are paper characteristics like moisture content, gloss, brightness, ink absorption, piling and picking tendencies; ink characteristics like tack, yield value, gloss, drying time, fineness of grind; fountain solution characteristics like pH and conductivity; roller characteristics like composition and Shore hardness; lot numbers of photographic films and presensitized plates, etc. Periodic checks should be made of the characteristics to assure their consistency.

## PROCESS CONTROL

Next to using the right materials, the most important facet of quality control is the control of the printing process by which the materials are used. To control the printing process, instruments, targets, scales and other devices are needed to provide objective measurements and numbers to characterize the process. The most important instrument for checking the consistency of a printing process is the *densitometer.*

**Densitometers** are photoelectric instruments for measuring optical density, or relative degree of light absorption or opacity of a subject. The darker the subject, the more light it absorbs and the higher is its optical density. There are special densitometers for measuring transmission and reflection densities of black-and-white and color subjects.

*Transmission densitometers* are used to control the photographic process by the use of gray scales and measurements of the graded steps in them before and after photography. Photography is controlled by varying exposure and development; the densitometer and gray scale help to verify the results.

*Reflection densitometers* are used to measure and control color proofs and sheets printed with special color bars, consisting of small blocks of each color, graded halftone tints and overprints of the colors. Measured are ink strength (color solids), dot gain (color tints) and ink trapping (color overprints) on the press. Most densitometers use filters for color measurement corresponding to the color separation filters (broad band) used in photography. Some densitometers use different lighting configurations to illuminate the area being measured, and some are equipped with special narrow band filters which give high readings and good correlation between densitometers for the reading of solid densities of 4-color process inks. There are other densitometers with polarizing filters which compensate for dryback of inks and also give higher readings. In comparing or correlating readings from different densitometers, it is important to consider the differences in illumination and filters between them.

**Control targets** besides gray scales and color bars are used as controls to standardize the process. *Sensitivity guides* are continuous-tone gray scales with numbered steps which are used to control exposures in platemaking and lithfilm photography. *Star targets* are pinwheels about ½″ in diameter, which are used to

SENSITIVITY GUIDE

STAR TARGET

DOT GAIN SCALE

measure image resolution during plate production and plate degradation, dot doubling, grain and slurring during printing. *Dot gain scales* consist of series of fine screen numbers from 0 to 9 in a coarse screen background which are used to determine plate sharpness and resolution during platemaking and either dot gain or plate wear on the press during printing. These and other control targets are supplied by the Graphic Arts Technical Foundation (GATF) and Rochester Institute of Technology.

**Quality control instruments** besides the densitometer are used to check raw materials and insure the stability of the printing process. *Paper hygroscopes* are hand held, sword-shaped instruments with hygroscopic elements, used to check the moisture balance of paper with the relative humidity of the atmosphere to assure printing without distortion, wrinkles and misregister. *Inkometers* are instruments with temperature controlled rollers and calibrated ink film thicknesses used to measure ink rheology, like tack and length used to check flow and trapping characteristics of inks. *Fineness of grind gauges* are steel blocks with two precision ground calibrated wedge grooves with depths ranging from 0 to 0.001 inch used with a scraper blade to determine the presence of improperly ground ink pigment particles. *Ink film thickness (IFT) gauges* are wheels with hubs and precision ground grooves like the fineness of grind gauge to measure the IFT on the steel roller above the ink form rollers. IFT is extremely important for consistent printing as it affects dot gain and plate wear. *Blanket packing gauges* are devices with micrometers used to control press packing by measuring plate and blanket height above or below the cylinder bearers. *pH meters* are electronic instruments used to measure and monitor the pH (acidity or alkalinity) of press fountain solutions which is important for consistent printing. Special precision 10- to 20-power *magnifying glasses* are important for the examination and analysis of printing defects and their causes.

## Standards and Tolerances

With the quality of raw materials assured and the process controlled as described, the setting of process standards and realistic tolerances for printing is straightforward. Process standards and tolerances vary with the type of product and the quality levels demanded. Some customer groups like the Magazine Publishers Association (MPA) have established standard ink colors for proofing for web offset known as SWOP. Register and color variation are two of the most critical characteristics requiring definition and specification. Commercial and hairline register are discussed on page 67. Acceptable *color variation* is generally ± 0.02 density units for the yellow, magenta and cyan, and ± 0.04 density units for the black.

## Inspection

Periodic inspection is necessary in any quality control system to make sure the printing system is functioning properly. *Quality cannot be inspected into printing jobs*. Unless there is strict adherence to raw material specifications, rigid control of process variables and realistic standards and tolerances, no amount of inspection will improve quality and reduce waste. When these facets of quality control are properly set and used, satisfactory printing becomes a matter of course, and periodic inspection is needed mainly to be sure the system does not go off-course.

# Binding

Some printing like stationery, small posters, notices, etc. can be delivered as printed, but most printing must be converted from printed sheets to a finished printed piece, through various binding and finishing operations. The work required to convert printed sheets or webs into books, magazines, catalogs and folders is called *binding*. The operations to make displays, folding cartons and boxes, tags, labels, greeting cards, and a variety of special packaging and advertising materials are known as *finishing*.

## PAMPHLET BINDING

This is a rather general term for binding folders, booklets, catalogs, magazines, etc., as opposed to bookbinding which will be discussed later. There are generally five steps in pamphlet binding: *scoring, folding, gathering* or *collating, stitching,* and *trimming.* Most printing requires one or more of these, but not necessarily all. For example, a printed folder, the simplest form of pamphlet binding, is trimmed to size and folded. When printed sheets are delivered to the bindery, the first step is to fold the sheets (in multiples of 4s) into sections or *signatures*. In the case of heavyweight or cover paper, folding is made easier by first scoring.

### Scoring

A score is defined as a crease in a sheet of heavyweight or cover paper to facilitate folding. As a rule, only those methods which produce an embossed ridge on the paper will give good folding results. The fold should always be made with the ridge or hinge on the inside for minimum stretch *(see illustrations)*. Booklet or catalog covers must have a score wide enough to take the necessary number of pages without strain on the fold.

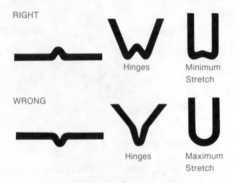

RIGHT

Hinges

Minimum Stretch

WRONG

Hinges

Maximum Stretch

The most common method of scoring is using a round face scoring rule locked in a form on a platen or cylinder press. The width of the rule varies with the thickness of the paper. A thicker paper requires a thicker rule which will give a wider crease to help make a cleaner fold.

### Folding

Paper is usually folded on a *buckle type* folding machine. The sheet is carried on conveyor belts from an automatic feeder, and rollers force the sheet into a fold-plate, which is adjustable to the length of the fold. The sheet hits a stop in the fold-plate, buckles, and is carried between two other rollers which fold the sheet. There can be as many as 64 pages to a signature.

FOLDER

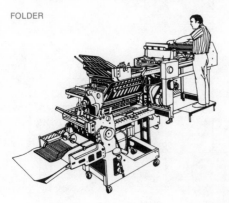

There are two kinds of folds: *parallel* and *right angle*. Parallel folding is just what the name implies, each fold is parallel to the other. An example would be a letter which requires two parallel folds for mailing. An *accordion* or *fan fold* is a type of parallel folding used extensively for computer printout forms. A right angle fold is two or more folds, with each fold at right angles to the preceding one. For example, most formal invitations are folded with two right angle folds.

Folding machines can be equipped with attachments for scoring, trimming, slitting, perforating and pasting. These are generally inexpensive and time saving.

In designing printing, the different types of folds and the limitations of mechanical folding should be considered at the planning level. Otherwise, one or more folds might end up being a costly hand-folding operation. The sketches on the following page illustrate the most common types of folds.

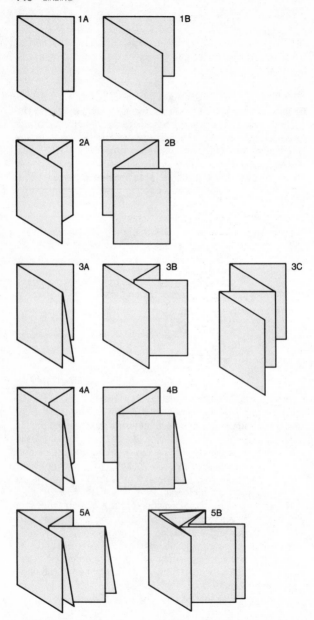

## Types of Folders

**1. Four-page folder** Simplest type of folder, with only one fold, folding either on the (A) long or (B) short dimension. Used for bill stuffers, instruction sheets, price lists, etc.

**2. Six-page folder** Made with two parallel folds, either (A) regular or (B) accordion. Used for letters, circulars, envelope stuffers, promotional folders, etc.

**3. Eight-page folder** Illustrated in three ways, (A) one parallel and one right angle fold, also called *french fold* when printing is on one side of the paper, (B) two parallel folds and (C) three parallel accordion folds, for ease in opening. Also, (A) and (B) can be bound into an 8-page booklet.

**4. Twelve-page folder** Illustrated in two ways, both with one parallel fold and two right angle folds, either (A) regular or (B) accordion. Sometimes used as 4-page letter, with the two right angle folds, folding letter to fit mailing envelope.

**5. Sixteen-page folder** Shown in two ways, (A) one parallel and two right angle folds and (B) three parallel folds, used for easy-to-open transportation schedules. Also, can be bound into a 16-page booklet.

## Collating

Once folded, the next step is to gather or collate the signatures in a predetermined order. The collating order should be checked to be sure of the correct sequence. Collating can be done by hand or machine, depending on the size of the job.

## Stitching

After the signatures are collated, they can be stitched together. There are two methods of stitching: *saddle-stitch* and *side-stitch*. The thickness or bulk of paper determines the style to be

SADDLE STITCHER

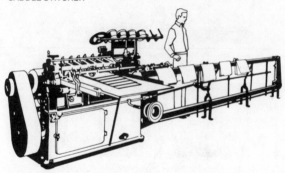

used. *Time* magazine is saddle-stitched; *National Geographic* is side-stitched.

In saddle-stitching, the booklet is placed on a saddle beneath a mechanical stitching head, and staples are forced through the backbone or spine of the booklet. This type of binding is the simplest and most inexpensive. Booklets will lie flat and stay open for ease in reading. Most booklets, programs and catalogs are saddle-stitched.

SADDLE-STITCH                    SIDE-STITCH

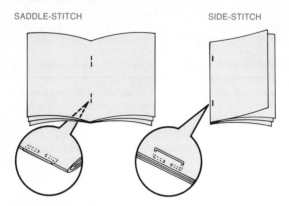

Side-stitching is used when the bulk is too great for saddle-stitching. The sections are collated, and then placed flat under a stitching head. Since the stitches are inserted about ¼″ from the back edge, the inside margin must be wider than in a saddle-stitched booklet. Side-stitched books cannot be completely opened flat and often have glued-on covers.

PAPER CUTTER

**Trimming or Cutting**

Three sides (top, bottom, right) of the booklet are trimmed on a guillotine-style paper cutter. For large-edition pamphlet binding, three-knife trimmers, which automatically trim three sides at one time are used. These are sometimes used as an attachment to the stitcher.

An automatic-spacing paper cutter is used for faster trimming of volume printing such as labels, leaflets, or any job printed in multiple form on the same sheet. This type of cutter automatically shifts to pre-set gauges after each cutting, resulting in greater uniformity and higher production.

## BOOKBINDING

There are many ways to bind a book, but the most common methods are: *edition binding*, also known as hardcover or case binding (best when permanence is required), *perfect binding* (widely used for inexpensive paperback books) and *mechanical binding* (for manuals and notebooks).

**Edition binding** The conventional method, which has been in use for many years, starts with the folding of printed sheets into 16- or 32-page signatures. Four-page *endleaves* are pasted on the outside of the first and last signatures. The signatures are then collated by machine and sewn together by special sewing machines designed for this purpose.

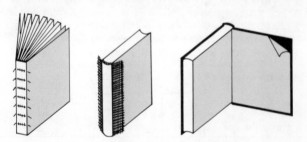

After they are sewn, the books are trimmed top, front and bottom, and the sewn edges are coated with glue. Each book is passed through a rounding machine which rolls the backbone. The rounded back is characteristic of this type of binding, and gives the book the correct shape to allow the cover to open and close properly. Next, a strip of gauze (super) is glued to the backbone in such a manner that the cloth extends outward from both sides of the backbone.

At the same time the books are being bound, the cloth covers *(cases)* are prepared on a case-making machine. Most covers are printed or stamped with some design and the title of the book. The printing is done on the cloth usually by the offset process and the stamping is done on a heavy-duty platen press using special dies and metallic foils. This is called *hot foil die stamping.* When the cover is finished, the book is automatically put into its case on a *casing-in* machine which applies paste to the endleaves and fits the cover into place.

The finished books are then dried in special hydraulic presses. Finally, they are inspected, wrapped in printed paper jackets, and packed for shipment. The school textbook and other hardbound books are examples of edition binding.

**Perfect binding** was developed to eliminate the expense of sewing and case-binding books. It is a variation of side-stitching and is widely used on paperback books. However, instead of being sewn or stitched, the pages are held together by a flexible adhesive. After the signatures are collated, the backs are ground off, leaving a rough surface. The adhesive is applied, a special lining is put over the backbone, and the cover is glued into place. The adhesive keeps its strength and resiliency for a long period of time. The *Pocket Pal* and the telephone book are examples of perfect binding.

**Mechanical binding** is used for notebooks and other types of books which must open flat. The sheets are punched with a series of round or slotted holes on the binding edge. Then wire, plastic coils or rings are inserted through the holes. Looseleaf notebooks are a form of mechanical binding with rings which

PLASTIC                                    SPIRAL

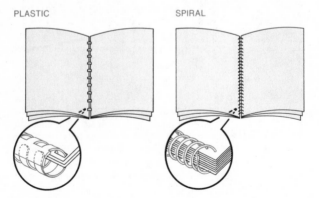

open to allow removal or addition of pages. In designing a book for mechanical binding, allowance must be made in the gutter (inner margin) of the book for the punched holes.

## FINISHING

As previously mentioned, finishing is a general term that includes a number of different operations and specialties. For instance, mounting, die-cutting and easeling of displays; varnishing, laminating, embossing, bronzing, die-stamping, pebbling, marbleizing, dyeing, stripping, folding, collating, punching, round cornering, padding, and tin-edging of printed and unprinted materials; cutting, creasing, stripping, and gluing of folding paper cartons; or slotting and gluing corrugated boxes. Most of these operations are highly specialized.

Some finishing operations are performed in-line with printing on web-fed presses. In newspaper, magazine and book printing, folded signatures are delivered from the press. In some types of packaging, particularly on flexographic presses, the cutting, creasing and stripping are done in-line with the printing. The new UV inks make possible in-line operations like lacquering, folding, slitting, etc., in sheet-fed printing.

Two finishing operations quite often used are embossing and die-cutting.

**Embossing** The image is molded in embossing so that it is raised in relief. Molding is achieved by pressing the material to be embossed between a brass female die and a male bed or counter mounted in register on a press. Strawboard, plastic, molding compound or newspaper matte material may be used for a counter. The counter is built up with layers of glued paper and shaped with an impression from the die on the press. All shoulders and squeezed material are cut away; pressure is applied only to the die area.

Light embossing may be done without heat on a cylinder or platen press. For heavy embossing and where fine detail is required, the die is fastened to a heated plate on a heavy-duty arch or *four-post* press. Embossing may be done in register with printing, or on blank stock giving a bas-relief effect. The latter is called *blind* embossing, and a soft paper is best. If a metallic effect is desired, special stamping foil is used.

**Die-cutting** There are two methods in use today: high or hollow die-cutting and steel rule die-cutting. Hollow die-cutting is a process used almost exclusively for labels and envelopes. A steel die, which is hollow like a cookie cutter, is positioned on a jogged pile of printed sheets. Pressure forces the die through the pile. The labels remain in the die until stripped out by hand.

Steel rule die-cutting is used for larger size dies or where close register is required. The dies are hardened steel rules bent to a desired shape and inserted into jigsawed gaps in ¾" plywood *dieboards*. The multiple dies are locked up in a chase. They are positioned and made ready on a platen die-cutting press. Flat-bed cylinder presses are also used for die-cutting. The ink rollers are removed to avoid being cut, and a steel jacket is secured around the cylinder. Die-cutting jackets are available to fit most presses and can be readily attached. Dies must have small nicks to prevent the die-cut area from dropping out while on press.

The latest developments in diecutting are laser-cut dieboards and rotary diecutters. In the laser cutting of dieboards, CAD/CAM techniques are used to layout the designs on the boards which are cut by high-powered lasers. Rotary diecutters are expensive and are used mainly on very long runs at high speed as an additional in-line operation on web presses for specialty products like milk cartons.

**Shrink-packaging** has been used in recent years to replace kraft paper packaging and banding of printed pieces. In addition to being able to see the product through the wrapping, its advantages are increased production and reduced labor cost. The equipment is simple to operate and inexpensive. Three essential units are needed: (1) a work table for dispensing the film and inserting the product; (2) an ''L'' bar heat sealer; (3) a shrink tunnel.

The product is inserted into a folded roll of polyethylene film which is heat-sealed around the product. It then goes into the shrink tunnel where the proper temperature shrinks the film tightly around the product. With proper equipment and film, almost any kind and shape of product can be shrink-packaged.

## BINDERY AUTOMATION

New equipment available for, and being installed in, printers' binderies include automatic units for counting, bundling and materials handling; automatic hopper loaders and bundle distribution systems; automatic palletizers and depalletizers; microprocessor-controlled cutting machines with automatic jogging, loading and unloading; folders with increasing speed and accuracy; automated adhesive binding systems; increased inline processing and computerized on-press addressing using ink jet printers.

# Paper

Paper, paperboard, or other stock on which an image is printed usually represents 30–50% of the final cost of a printed job. Besides the cost, the paper's characteristics can have a significant bearing on the appearance of the job and the printer's ability to print it. Since paper is one of the most important parts of a printed piece, everyone involved should know as much as possible about its manufacture and characteristics so that the proper paper is selected. The paper chosen should have the desired printability and runnability so that optimum results and minimum problems are encountered in the printing.

## PULPING

The first step in papermaking is the production of pulp, and wood is by far the most widely used raw material. Wood, however, differs from northern to southern climates, necessitating different processes for making satisfactory pulp. In some parts of the world where wood is not readily available other fiber sources are utilized, such as bagasse (sugar cane), bamboo, esparto and hemp. Faster growing sources of pulp like *kenaf* are also being developed. There are four types of pulping processes: *mechanical, chemical, semi-chemical,* and *thermomechanical.*

**Mechanical pulping** produces groundwood pulp. Cleaned and peeled logs are ground against a revolving grindstone or wood chips are passed between two steel discs or a refiner until they are reduced to fiber. Groundwood pulp is economical since all the wood is used. It does, however, contain impurities which can cause discoloration and weakening of the paper. Its main uses are for newsprint, and as part of the pulp in magazine papers where it contributes bulk, opacity and compressibility.

**Chemical pulping** removes most of the impurities such as lignin, resins, gums and other undesirable components of the wood so that the pulp is mainly cellulose fiber. Papers made from this pulp are much more permanent than groundwood paper. Chemical pulping is done by cooking wood chips with chemicals in batch or continuous digesters. There are two main types of chemical wood pulp: *sulfite* and *sulfate.* Sulfite pulp is made by cooking chips of coniferous woods like spruce, pine and hemlock in a liquor made from lime and sulfurous acid. Sulfate pulp, also known as kraft, is produced by cooking broadleaf or coniferous woods with caustic soda and sodium sulfide. Since sulfate pulp uses a wider variety of woods and produces a stronger paper, it is used more widely than sulfite pulp.

**Semi-chemical pulping** combines chemical with mechanical pulping to produce a pulp with higher yield yet somewhat similar properties to chemical pulp. It is a treatment for hardwoods and is usually used as a blend with chemical pulp imparting stiffness and good formation.

**Thermo-mechanical pulping (TMP)** is a new form of mechanical pulping involving the hot pressurized refining of wood chips. Stone grinding of logs causes considerable damage to fibers producing fiber bundles called *shives* and wood debris, called *fines*. The pulp produced in this manner is weak and must be strengthened with chemical pulp. By using wood chips and a refiner and steam pressurizing the chip feeder and refiner, superior groundwood is produced with a yield of over 90% from the wood. The strength, particularly tear, is improved considerably and the pulp is strong enough to be used for newsprint without the addition of chemical pulp.

## BLEACHING

Bleaching is a further step in the purification of fibers and is responsible for higher brightness in papers. While pure cellulose is white in color, the presence of impurities and coloring matter gives the pulp a brownish color, as in grocery bags, which are made from unbleached kraft pulp. Chemical pulps are bleached in multiple stage processes (3–7 stages) with chemicals like chlorine, chlorine dioxide, and/or sodium hypochlorite, with alternate treatments in caustic soda and washing with water. The latest development in bleaching is the use of oxygen in the chlorine bleach cycle.

## BEATING, REFINING AND SIZING

Beating and refining are important steps in papermaking since the characteristics of the paper are largely determined by the treatment of the pulp in these operations.

Beating is performed in an oval tub in which a large batch of pulp is circulated by means of a revolving roll. Refining is done in closed conical shaped units. In both cases the pulp is passed between a rotating and a stationary set of steel bars which cause cutting, bruising and crushing of the fibers. The treatment is controlled to produce the desired strength and other qualities in the finished paper. Refining is a continuous process permitting fast changes in paper characteristics and has largely replaced beating.

In addition to the mechanical treatment of the pulp, certain materials are added to impart other characteristics which make the product more suitable for its intended use. Rosin size is added to give water repellency so that the paper can be used for pen and ink writing, offset printing or resistance to weather. Fillers, such as clay, are used to improve smoothness, opacity and affinity for ink; titanium dioxide for opacity and brightness. Dyes and pigments are also added to control the color shade or to produce colored papers, and alum is added to fix the size and color on the fibers. The combination of fiber, size, fillers and alum is known as *stock,* and this is stored in large tanks or chests ahead of the paper machine.

## MAKING PAPER

The modern Fourdrinier paper machine is extremely complex but consists essentially of three principal units: (1) the paper-forming section, known as the wet end (2) the press section, where water is removed by pressing the wet paper between rolls and felts and (3) the drying section, where the moisture content is reduced to the desired level.

**Fourdrinier Wet End** The stock from the machine chest is diluted with water and pumped to a distribution unit or headbox. This spreads the flow to the width of the machine and discharges it through an orifice onto a finely woven endless wire belt. The water is drained through the wire by gravity and suction, leaving the stock on the surface. The fibers tend to align themselves in the direction the machine is traveling. To prevent this and improve the formation, the headbox end of the wire section is given a side-by-side shaking motion. Some machines, especially for offset newsprint, are equipped with two wires and are known as *twin-wire* machines.

DRY END OF A
PAPER MACHINE

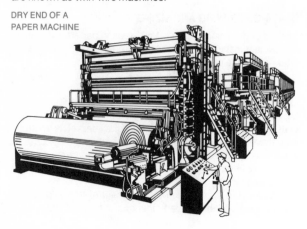

**Dandy Roll** This roll consists of a cylindrical frame covered with wire mesh and is located on top of the wire between two of the suction boxes. At this point the sheet is still wet enough to be compressed by the weight of the roll which helps distribute the fibers and improve formation. In some cases the surface of the roll contains lettering or a design, and this type of dandy roll produces a watermarked paper.

**Press Section** The web of paper as it leaves the wire still contains 75–85% water, and this is reduced to 60–70% in the press section. The operation is performed in a series of presses, each consisting of two rolls, and the sheet passes through the nip between these rolls supported on a felt belt made mainly of wool. Removal of water by pressing is more economical than by drying; the presses compact the sheet and level the surface.

**Machine Drying** From the presses the paper enters the drying sections where the sheet is dried to the final moisture content. The driers are steam-heated cast iron drums, four to six feet in diameter, polished on the outside surface. The drums are generally arranged in two tiers with as many as thirty tiers of driers on some of the larger installations. On paper machines the sheet is held tightly against the driers by a heavy felt usually made of cotton or cotton-asbestos. About two pounds of water are evaporated for each pound of paper produced.

**Calendering and Supercalendering** Calendering is the last operation on the paper machine before the paper is wound on reels. Supercalendering is a subsequent operation. Machine calenders are stacks of vertical cast steel rolls that have polished ground surfaces. The paper enters the stack at the top and is compacted and smoothed progressively as it travels on the way down the stack. Calendered papers are known as *machine finished papers*. Supercalenders are also arranged vertically, but the rolls are alternately steel and either cotton or compressed air. Supercalenders are used for both coated and uncoated papers.

### Coated Papers

The great popularity of reproducing black-and-white and color photographs brought about the development of coated papers. These grades reproduce much finer halftone screens with sharper definition, improved density and greater color fidelity that can be reproduced on uncoated papers. Coated paper finishes range from dull to very glossy, have a greater affinity for printing inks, greater smoothness, higher opacity, and better ink holdout than uncoated papers.

Coated printing papers are available coated one side only (C1S) for labels, packaging and covers; or coated two sides (C2S) for book, publication and commercial printing. Papers coated on the machine are called *machine coated;* those coated on independent coaters are said to be *off-machine coated.*

Coatings consist of suspensions of pigments in suitable binders. They are applied by rolls, air knives, or by trailing blades. Blade coatings have become very popular as they are smoother, and it is possible to apply lower coat weights which are necessary for lighter weight publication grades.

## Paper Finishes

Finish is a complex paper property related to its smoothness. Paper can be used as it comes off the driers of a paper machine, or it can be machine calendered and then later supercalendered. Uncalendered, machine calendered and supercalendered papers vary greatly in smoothness.

The usual finishes of uncoated book papers are, in order of increasing smoothness: *antique, eggshell, vellum, machine finish (MF).* These finishes are classed together because all can be produced on the machine. Additional smoothness is obtained with supercalendering. Coating, of course, further improves the finish and smoothness.

Some finishes are embossed on the paper after it leaves the machine. These are produced by a rotary embosser, a machine similar to a mangle, with the paper passing through it dry and under pressure. Commonly used embossing patterns are linen, tweed, and pebble.

## Top (Felt) Side and Wire Side

Paper is considered a two-sided material. Each side has different characteristics. These are due to the way paper is made. The side directly in contact with the wire of the paper machine is called the *wire side,* the other side is the top or *felt side.* The felt side usually has a closer formation with less grain and better crossing of the fibers. The wire side, however, has less fines on the surface and usually gives less trouble in the depositing of loose paper dust, fiber picking or lint on the blanket of an offset press.

The paper produced on twin-wire machines has less *two-sidedness* than paper produced on conventional machines. Both sides are more similar to the wire side in that they have less fines and cause less problems with lint, etc. on offset press blankets. This paper is used extensively for newsprint in web offset printing.

## PAPER CHARACTERISTICS

**Grain** is an important factor for both printing and binding. It refers to the position of the fibers. During papermaking most fibers are oriented with their length parallel to that of the paper machine and their width running across the machine. In other words, the grain of the sheet is in the *machine direction;* the other dimension is called the *cross direction.*

Grain affects paper in the following ways, and these facts need to be considered in the proper use of paper: (1) Paper folds smoothly *with* the grain direction and roughens or cracks when folding cross-grain. This is often important in planning a printed piece. (2) Paper is stiffer in the grain direction. (3) Paper expands or contracts more in the cross direction when exposed to moisture changes.

TEAR AND FOLD TESTS

Paper tears straighter with grain

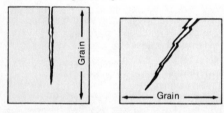

Paper folds more easily with grain

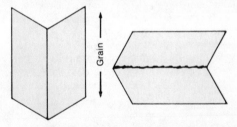

In books and catalogs, grain direction should be parallel with the binding edge. If it is perpendicular with the binding edge, the pages turn less easily and do not lie flat. Paper for sheet-fed offset is usually grain long. Moisture changes affect the shorter dimension and register problems are reduced. A second reason for grain long is that the sidewise size of printed images cannot be changed without cutting or changing plates, whereas changing the size of the printed image around the cylinder (short dimension of the sheet) can be accomplished by changing the packing under the plate and blanket.

**Basis weight** With few exceptions, printing papers are manufactured and identified by their *basis weight*. In the U.S. it is the weight in pounds of a ream (500 sheets) in the *basic size* for that grade. In the Metric System it is the weight of one square meter of paper and is expressed in grams per square meter or $g/m^2$. Basis 70 means that 500 sheets 25 x 38 of book paper weigh 70 pounds. This is equivalent to 104 $g/m^2$ in the Metric System.

In the U.S. System the basic size is *not* the same for all grades: It is 25 x 38 for book papers (coated, text, offset, opaque, etc.); 17 x 22 for writing papers (bond, ledger, mimeograph, duplicator); 20 x 26 for cover papers (coated and uncoated); 25½ x 30½ for index bristol; 22½ x 28½ or 22½ x 35 for mill bristol and postcard; 24 x 36 for tag and newsprint.

Paper is commonly identified by ream weight: 20-pound bond, 70-pound coated, etc. However, paper is usually listed in size-and-weight tables and price lists on a thousand sheet basis: 25 x 38—140M for a 70-pound book paper, the "M" meaning 1,000 sheets 25 x 38 weigh 140 pounds. Each grade is made in many standard sizes other than the basic size, and in many weights. For example, book papers are made in weights from 50–pound to 100–pound in 10–pound increments.

**Metric system** In the metric system which is used today by most countries other than the U.S., basis weight or substance is referred to as *grammage* and is expressed as weight per unit area, or grams per square meter ($g/m^2$). Such measurements are independent of paper size. There is, however, a basic size of paper in the metric system known as the A series and while its area is a square meter it is not a meter square. The series consists of sheet sizes in which the area from one size to the next varies by a factor of 2 or ½. Following is a table of the A sizes.

| A number | Size (Millimeters) | (Inches) | Area (Square Meters) |
|---|---|---|---|
| A0 | 841 x 1189 | 33.1 x 46.8 | 1.0 |
| A1 | 594 x 841 | 23.4 x 33.1 | 0.5 |
| A2 | 420 x 594 | 16.5 x 23.4 | 0.25 |
| A3 | 297 x 420 | 11.7 x 16.5 | 0.125 |
| A4 | 210 x 297 | 8.3 x 11.7 | 0.063 |
| A5 | 148 x 210 | 5.8 x 8.3 | 0.031 |

This is part of the basic A series. There are others such as B sizes which are intermediate between the A sizes, RA and SRA stock sizes from which A sizes can be cut and C series for envelopes and folders suitable for stationery in the A sizes. The standard size in the metric system which corresponds closely to the U.S. 8½″ x 11″ size is A4.

The following table will help paper users and producers to convert basis weights of paper from the U.S. System to the Metric System and vice versa:

| Trade Size | Conversion Factor | |
|---|---|---|
| | Metric to U.S. $(g/m^2 \text{ to lbs.})$ | U.S. to Metric $(\text{lbs. to } g/m^2)$ |
| 17 x 22 | 0.266 | 3.760 |
| 20 x 26 | 0.370 | 2.704 |
| 24 x 36 | 0.614 | 1.627 |
| 25 x 38 | 0.675 | 1.480 |
| 1000 ft.$^2$ | 0.205 | 4.831 |

A simple way to convert approximately the basic weight for 25 x 38 paper to $g/m^2$ is to multiply it by 1½ or ³⁄₂. 40 lb. book paper is roughly 60 $g/m^2$ paper. According to the table it is $40 \times 1.48 = 59.2 \, g/m^2$. Conversely to convert $g/m^2$ to lbs/ream 25 x 38 paper, multiply by ⅔. 45 $g/m^2$ paper is approximately 30 lb. paper. According to the table it is $45 \times 0.675 = 30.8$.

**Thickness and bulk** Thickness is often referred to as caliper and is measured in mils or thousandths of an inch. In book manufacturing, the bulk of the paper determines the thickness of the book so it is often expressed in different terms than the thickness or caliper of the sheet. Bulk for book papers is expressed as the number of pages per inch (ppi) for a given basis weight. For example, the bulking range for a 50–pound book paper can be from 310 to 800 ppi.

**Strength** The strength of paper is more dependent on the nature of its fiber than its thickness. High bursting strength is achieved by closely intermingling long pulp fibers during the forming of the sheet on the paper machine wire. Some papers, paper bags for example, need high tearing resistance. Fibers are long, and tear in the cross-machine direction is always higher than tear in the machine direction. This is so because the greatest number of fibers lie *across* the path of the cross-machine tear.

Papers which are subjected to considerable tension in use, such as those printed on web presses, should have a high tensile strength as well as high tear strength.

**Stretch** is the amount of distortion paper undergoes under tensile strain. Stretch is generally much greater in the cross direction than in the machine direction.

## RUNNABILITY AND PRINT QUALITY

Two important factors that affect the printing of papers by any process are *runnability* and *print quality.* Runnability affects the ability to get the paper through the press and failures in runnability can cause expensive downtime. Print quality factors affect the appearance of the printed image on the paper.

### Runnability

This is more of a problem in offset than in letterpress or gravure because of the overall contact of the paper with the blanket during impression, and the use of water and tacky inks. The following paper properties can affect runnability:

**Flatness** Freedom from buckles, puckers, wave and curl — especially important in offset.

**Trimming** Sheets should be square, accurate in size.

**Dirt** Loose material from all manufacturing sources, such as slitter and trimmer dust, lint, loose pigments or loosely bonded fibers on the surface — especially troublesome in offset.

**Moisture content or RH** The paper should be in balance with the pressroom RH. An increase in RH can cause *wavy edges;* the edges absorb moisture while the rest of the pile remains unchanged. *Tight edges,* in which the edges lose moisture and contract, are caused when the RH of the pressroom is lower than the paper. Both wavy and tight edges can cause wrinkles and/or misregister in printing, especially in offset.

IMPROPERLY CONDITIONED PAPER

Wavy edges                     Tight edges

**Adequate pick resistance** Weak paper surfaces tend to pick, blister, delaminate, or split when tacky ink is transferred from the plate or blanket to the paper. This is more of a problem in offset than in letterpress.

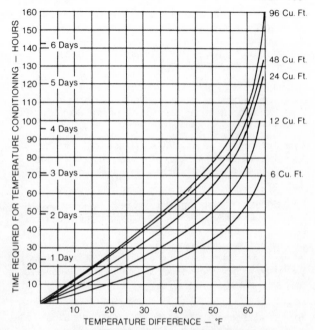

TEMPERATURE CONDITIONING CHART FOR PAPER
*Courtesy of Graphic Arts Technical Foundation, Inc.*

**Adequate water resistance** Lithographic papers with soluble or water-sensitive coatings tend to pile on the blanket necessitating frequent stops for washups. The piling can occur in the image or non-image areas. Each is caused by different paper properties, and the exact cause is not known for sure.

**Paper-ink affinity** Paper surfaces can affect ink drying, chalking, rub-off, set-off, ink and varnish holdout.

**Mechanical condition** Paper should be free of holes, wrinkles, torn sheets, scraps, turned-over corners, stuck spots or edges and foreign matter. Paper rolls should be evenly and tightly wound with smooth even edges and a minimum of splices.

## Print Quality

The appearance characteristics of the printed image can be affected by the following paper properties. These are especially important when the same job is being printed in more than one plant or when a job is being reprinted.

**Color** Paper color is important as it affects the color reproduction of lighter tints especially. Paper colors vary with advertising fads from cool to warm shades. Type is more easily read against a soft (yellowish) white, while process colors reproduce most accurately on neutral white paper.

**Brightness** affects the contrast, brilliance, snap or sparkle of the printed subject. Artificial brighteners, like flourescent additives, can affect color reproduction as most are not neutral in color and have excess blue reflectance.

**Opacity** relates to the *show-through* of the printed image from the opposite side of the sheet or the sheet under it. It is affected by the thickness of the sheet and the use of mineral fillers like titanium dioxide.

**Smoothness** is a very important property for letterpress and gravure but has little effect on offset. Smooth surfaces have irregularities of the order of 0.005″ to 0.010″ apart. They cannot be seen by the naked eye, but can be detected by a magnifying glass and low angle illumination. As smoothness decreases, solids and halftones get sandy and rough in appearance but type is not affected much.

**Gloss** affects the appearance of the ink film. Coupled with ink absorption, it can be used as a measure of paper surface efficiency (PSE) or the purity of ink reproduction.

**Refractiveness** relates to light absorption in the surface of the paper causing halftones to appear darker than they should.

**Web offset paper** naturally has its grain direction paralleling the web. The printer and paper mill must work together on the specifications for each order. Rolls must be properly wound, protected, stored on end, and have good tensile strength to minimize tearing or breaking of the web on press. Paper should be uniform caliper (thickness); be free from holes, scum spots, slitter dust, fiber picking, and lint; have a minimum of contraction and expansion; contain a minimum number of splices; and have sound cores for winding and delivery.

## PAPER TESTING AND EVALUATION FOR PRINTABILITY

Printing papers are tested for a number of properties, namely: basis weight, brightness, caliper, gloss, oil absorption, opacity, porosity, smoothness, stiffness, tear, tensile strength. While all of these tests are valuable for mill quality control and product uniformity, they are generally useless for predicting the printing characteristics of the paper. Much printability testing has been done, and many testers have been designed and built. But the most reliable testing for lithography, especially, is still done on a production printing press.

Most letterpress testing for smoothness, ink receptivity, and coverage can be done on special test proof presses. Printability testers can be used to make reasonably accurate predictions of picking, ink coverage, receptivity, and, with new models, even trapping has been predicted with some degree of success. There are special printability testers for gravure.

For lithography, however, printability testers are far from having the reliability desired mainly because the effects of dampening have been difficult to stimulate. Therefore, most printability testing is done on an offset press. Many laboratories are working on the development of bench or proof press tests that correlate with performance on the press. As yet none has been completely successful.

## PAPER GRADES

Paper may be defined in terms of its use. Each grade serves a purpose, usually suggested by its grade name. Some of the most common classifications of printing papers are: bond, coated, text, cover, book, offset, index, label, tag and newsprint. The size shown in parentheses is the basic size for that grade.

**Bond (17 x 22)** Bond papers are commonly used for letters and business forms. They have surfaces which accept ink readily from a pen or typewriter and can be easily erased. Most letterheads and business forms are a standard 8½ x 11 size.

**Coated (25 x 38)** This consists of base paper to which has been applied a smooth, glossy coating. Coated papers are used when high printing quality is desired because of its greater surface smoothness and uniform ink receptivity. There are many kinds: cast coated, gloss coated, dull coated, machine coated, coated one and two sides, etc.

**Text (25 x 38)** These papers are noted for their interesting textures and attractive colors. They enjoy frequent use for announcements, booklets and brochures. Most text papers are treated with a sizing to make them more resistant to water penetration and easier to print to offset lithography.

**Book (25 x 38)** These papers are used for trade and textbooks as well as general printing. They are less expensive than text papers, and are made in antique or smooth finishes. Book papers have a wider range of weights and bulk than text papers so it is possible to secure almost any desired bulking.

**Offset (25 x 38)** Similar to the coated and uncoated book paper used for letterpress printing except that sizing is added to resist the slight moisture present in offset printing, and the surface is treated to resist picking.

**Cover (20 x 26)** Coated and text papers are made in heavier weights and matching colors for use as covers on booklets, etc. Papers are also made for cover purposes only. Many special surface textures are available, with finishes ranging from antique to smooth. Special characteristics of cover pages include dimensional stability, durability, uniform printing surface, good scoring, folding, embossing and die-cutting qualities. It is a useful rule of thumb that cover stock of the same basis weight as text paper has about twice the thickness.

**Index (22½ x 35 and 25½ x 30½)** Two outstanding characteristics are stiffness and receptivity to writing ink. Commonly used whenever an inexpensive stiff paper is required. Available in both smooth and vellum finish.

**Tag (24 x 36)** A utility sheet ranging in weight from 100 to 250 pounds for manufacturing tags. It may be made from sulfite, sulfate or mechanical pulp, and various types of waste papers. Tag board is sometimes tinted and colored on one or both sides. Tag stock has good bending or folding qualities, suitable bursting and tensile strength, good tearing and water resistance, and a surface adaptable to printing, stamping, or writing.

**Bristol (22½ x 28½)** One of the board grades, bristol has a softer surface than index or tag, making it ideal for high speed folding, embossing or stamping. It is an economical substitute for cotton fiber stocks, is very receptive to ink and has good snap and resilience.

**Newsprint (24 x 36)** Paper used in printing newspapers. Furnish is chiefly groundwood pulp, with some chemical pulp. It is made in basis weights from 28 to 35 pounds, with 30–pound used most extensively.

**Lightweight Papers** Such as manifold, onionskin and bible paper are specialty grades that have been produced for years. Recently increasing mailing costs have fostered the development and use of lighter weight newsprint and magazine papers. Newsprint as light as 22 pound ($36g/m^2$) has been produced; 32 pound ($47g/m^2$) coated magazine paper is used regularly in web offset, and 28 pound ($41g/m^2$) paper in gravure.

## CUTTING CHARTS

A smart paper buyer always tries to use standard paper sizes which can be used without waste. Odd size pages can be wasteful and costly if the quantity is not large enough, or if there is not enough time to order a special-making size of paper.

This chart shows the number of pages to a standard paper size for several page sizes in use today. The paper size includes trim top, bottom and side, but *not* bleed.

| Trimmed Page Size | Number of Printed Pages | Number From Sheet | Standard Paper Size |
|---|---|---|---|
| | 4 | 12 | 25 x 38 |
| | 8 | 12 | 38 x 50 |
| 4 x 9 | 12 | 4 | 25 x 38 |
| | 16 | 6 | 38 x 50 |
| | 24 | 2 | 25 x 38 |
| | 4 | 32 | 35 x 45 |
| 4¼ x 5⅜ | 8 | 16 | 35 x 45 |
| | 16 | 8 | 35 x 45 |
| | 32 | 4 | 35 x 45 |
| | 4 | 16 | 25 x 38 |
| 4½ x 6 | 8 | 8 | 25 x 35 |
| | 16 | 4 | 25 x 38 |
| | 32 | 2 | 25 x 38 |
| | 4 | 16 | 35 x 45 |
| 5½ x 8½ | 8 | 8 | 35 x 45 |
| | 16 | 4 | 35 x 45 |
| | 32 | 2 | 35 x 45 |
| | 4 | 8 | 25 x 38 |
| 6 x 9 | 8 | 4 | 25 x 38 |
| | 16 | 2 | 25 x 38 |
| | 32 | 2 | 38 x 50 |
| | 4 | 4 | 23 x 35 |
| 8½ x 11 | 8 | 2 | 23 x 35 |
| | 16 | 2 | 35 x 45 |
| | 4 | 4 | 25 x 38 |
| 9 x 12 | 8 | 2 | 25 x 38 |
| | 16 | 2 | 38 x 50 |

## EQUIVALENT WEIGHTS

In reams of 500 sheets, basis weights in bold type.

| Grade of Paper | BOOK 25 x 38 | BOND 17 x 22 | COVER 20 x 26 | BRISTOL 22½ x 28½ | INDEX 25½ x 30½ | TAG 24 x 36 | GRAMMAGE (g/m²) |
|---|---|---|---|---|---|---|---|
| **BOOK** | **30** | 12 | 16 | 20 | 25 | 27 | 44 |
| | **40** | 16 | 22 | 27 | 33 | 36 | 59 |
| | **45** | 18 | 25 | 30 | 37 | 41 | 67 |
| | **50** | 20 | 27 | 34 | 41 | 45 | 74 |
| | **60** | 24 | 33 | 40 | 49 | 55 | 89 |
| | **70** | 28 | 38 | 47 | 57 | 64 | 104 |
| | **80** | 31 | 44 | 54 | 65 | 73 | 118 |
| | **90** | 35 | 49 | 60 | 74 | 82 | 133 |
| | **100** | 39 | 55 | 67 | 82 | 91 | 148 |
| | **120** | 47 | 66 | 80 | 98 | 109 | 178 |
| **BOND** | 33 | **13** | 18 | 22 | 27 | 30 | 49 |
| | 41 | **16** | 22 | 27 | 33 | 37 | 61 |
| | 51 | **20** | 28 | 34 | 42 | 46 | 75 |
| | 61 | **24** | 33 | 41 | 50 | 56 | 90 |
| | 71 | **28** | 39 | 48 | 58 | 64 | 105 |
| | 81 | **32** | 45 | 55 | 67 | 74 | 120 |
| | 91 | **36** | 50 | 62 | 75 | 83 | 135 |
| | 102 | **40** | 56 | 69 | 83 | 93 | 158 |
| **COVER** | 91 | 36 | **50** | 62 | 75 | 82 | 135 |
| | 110 | 43 | **60** | 74 | 90 | 100 | 163 |
| | 119 | 47 | **65** | 80 | 97 | 108 | 176 |
| | 146 | 58 | **80** | 99 | 120 | 134 | 216 |
| | 164 | 65 | **90** | 111 | 135 | 149 | 243 |
| | 183 | 72 | **100** | 124 | 150 | 166 | 271 |
| **BRISTOL** | 100 | 39 | 54 | **67** | 81 | 91 | 148 |
| | 120 | 47 | 65 | **80** | 98 | 109 | 178 |
| | 148 | 58 | 81 | **100** | 121 | 135 | 219 |
| | 176 | 70 | 97 | **120** | 146 | 162 | 261 |
| | 207 | 82 | 114 | **140** | 170 | 189 | 306 |
| | 237 | 93 | 130 | **160** | 194 | 216 | 351 |
| **INDEX** | 110 | 43 | 60 | 74 | **90** | 100 | 163 |
| | 135 | 53 | 74 | 91 | **110** | 122 | 203 |
| | 170 | 67 | 93 | 115 | **140** | 156 | 252 |
| | 208 | 82 | 114 | 140 | **170** | 189 | 328 |
| **TAG** | 110 | 43 | 60 | 74 | 90 | **100** | 163 |
| | 137 | 54 | 75 | 93 | 113 | **125** | 203 |
| | 165 | 65 | 90 | 111 | 135 | **150** | 244 |
| | 192 | 76 | 105 | 130 | 158 | **175** | 284 |
| | 220 | 87 | 120 | 148 | 180 | **200** | 326 |
| | 275 | 109 | 151 | 186 | 225 | **250** | 407 |

## Comparative Weights of Book Papers per 1,000 Sheets

| Basis | 50 | 60 | 70 | 80 | 100 | 120 |
|---|---|---|---|---|---|---|
| 8½ x 11 | 9.8 | 11.8 | 13.8 | 15.7 | 19.7 | 23.6 |
| 17½ x 22½ | 41 | 50 | 58 | 66 | 83 | 99 |
| 19 x 25 | 50 | 60 | 70 | 80 | 100 | 120 |
| 23 x 29 | 70 | 84 | 98 | 112 | 140 | 169 |
| 23 x 35 | 85 | 102 | 119 | 136 | 169 | 203 |
| 24 x 36 | 90 | 110 | 128 | 146 | 182 | 218 |
| 25 x 38 | 100 | 120 | 140 | 160 | 200 | 240 |
| 35 x 45 | 166 | 198 | 232 | 266 | 332 | 398 |
| 36 x 48 | 182 | 218 | 254 | 292 | 364 | 436 |
| 38 x 50 | 200 | 240 | 280 | 320 | 400 | 480 |
| *metric (g/m²) | 74 | 89 | 104 | 118 | 148 | 178 |

*Metric equivalent of basis weight.

## ENVELOPE STYLES

**A. Commercial** envelopes are used for business correspondence, either surface or airmail. Made in bond and kraft papers in all standard sizes.

**B. Window** envelopes are used primarily for statements, dividends and invoices. The window saves time and prevents an element of error by eliminating typing of an extra address. Window envelopes are made in all sizes, papers and styles.

**C. Self-Sealing** envelopes have latex adhesive on upper and lower flaps that seal instantly without moisture when flaps come together. These envelopes are a time saver in handling.

**D. Booklet, Open-Side** envelopes are ideal for direct mail and house organs. Concealed seam lends itself to overall printing in front and back.

**E. Baronial** envelopes are a more formal open-side envelope with a deep, pointed flap. They are often used for invitations, greeting cards, announcements, etc.

**F. Bankers Flap and Wallet Flap** envelopes handle unusually bulky correspondence. Can be crammed with correspondence and will carry material safely. Reserve strength is far in excess of everyday commercial envelopes.

**G. Clasp and String-and-Button** envelopes are sturdy and widely used for mailing bulky papers. Metal clasps are smooth and burrless. String and button keep contents under tension and better protected in the mail. Both types may be opened and closed many times.

**H. Open End** envelopes are used for mailing catalogs, reports, booklets and magazines. Wide seams and heavy gummed flaps insure maximum protection under rough handling conditions.

**I. Expansion** envelopes are used for bulky correspondence and for package and rack sales.

ENVELOPE STYLES

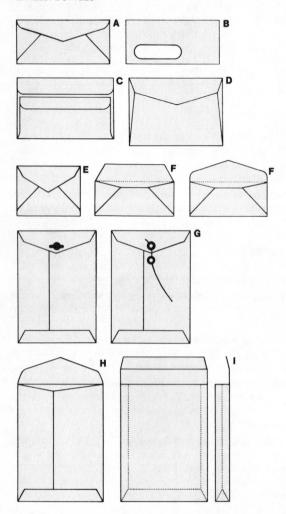

# Printing inks

Each printing process requires different inks to produce printed images. In general all inks consist of pigments, resin vehicles in which the pigment is dispersed, solvents or other fluids to control body, and other additives to induce drying and/or impart necessary working properties to the inks. Letterpress and lithographic inks are fairly stiff and require long ink roller trains on the press to get the proper flow and film thickness for printing. Gravure and flexographic inks are very fluid and dry mainly by evaporation of solvent. Screen printing inks are paint-like in consistency and drying characteristics.

The most important properties of ink are *color, color strength, body, length, tack* and *drying* characteristics.

**Pigments** are finely divided solid materials which give inks color and other optical properties like opacity or transparency. Some pigments like alumina hydrate, chrome yellow and iron blues are inorganic but most of the pigments in use are insoluble derivatives of organic dyes. In addition to color, important pigment characteristics include specific gravity, particle size, opacity, chemical resistance, wettability and permanence. The colorants used in heat transfer printing are special sublimable dyes which under heat and pressure, sublime and transfer from the paper print to textile surfaces containing polyesters.

**Color matching** has been traditionally done by visual comparison under standard lighting conditions. Most color matching is now done with spectrophotometers and computer programs. Color matching systems using sets of basic inks, color charts and mixing formulas are offered by Pantone (PMS) and Metricolor and are used for customer specification of colors.

**Body** refers to the consistency, stiffness or softness of inks. Ink consistencies vary widely from very stiff inks for collotype to very soft, fluid inks for newsprint, gravure and flexography. Associated with the body is the term *viscosity* which is a means of measuring the flow characteristics of soft or fluid inks. Stiff inks can have a false body which is called *thixotropy*. Conventional letterpress and offset inks are shear thinning. They set to a fairly stiff mass in the can but when they are worked on a slab with an ink knife they become quite fluid and flow freely.

**Length** is a property associated with the ability of an ink to flow and form filaments. Inks can be *long* or *short*. Long inks flow well and form long filaments. They are undesirable, especially on high-speed presses because they have a tendency to *fly* or *mist*. Newsprint inks are characterized by this property. Short inks

LONG INK                              SHORT INK

have the consistency of butter with poor flow properties. They have a tendency to pile on the rollers, plate or blanket. Most satisfactory inks are neither excessively long nor short.

**Tack** is the *stickiness* of the ink, or the force required to split an ink film between two surfaces. It is an important requirement in the transfer of ink in the ink train to the plate and then from the plate to the paper in letterpress or from the plate to the blanket and the blanket to the paper in offset. Tack is also important in determining whether the ink will pick the surface of the paper, will trap properly in wet multicolor printing, or will print sharp, clean lines and halftones. If the tack of the ink is higher than the surface strength of the paper, the paper will pick, split or tear. In wet multicolor printing as in letterpress and lithography the first ink down must be tackier than the next ink at the instant of trans- fer, or the second ink will not transfer to (trap on) the first color. Offset inks must be tacky to print sharp images and resist exces- sive emulsification with the fountain solution. Compromises must be reached when jobs contain both solids and halftones since tacky inks do not print smooth solids. Ink tack can be measured on an Inkometer or Tackoscope.

**Drying** of inks is important because a printed piece cannot be handled or used until the liquid or plastic ink film has solidified and dried. Printing inks dry in a number of ways: absorption, selective absorption, oxidation, polymerization, evaporation and precipitation. Most inks dry by a combination of two or more of these mechanisms. The first stage in drying is setting, and often this is more important in printing than the actual drying.

New systems for drying or curing inks have been developed to eliminate pollution caused by the evolution of solvents and other effluents associated with ink drying. New inks that cure by UV and/or electron beam (EB) radiation are described on page 178. New infrared units have been developed for drying special inks of the low solvent super quick-setting type. In-line overcoatings are used to eliminate anti-set off sprays and assist drying in sheet-fed printing *(see page 181).*

INKOMETER

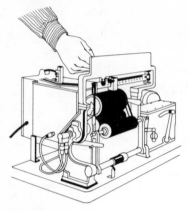

**Planning** When a job is first planned, ''thinking ink'' can avoid a lot of headaches and expense later. Remember that the inkmaker must mate the ink to the paper. Their relationship is critical. Color matches for small amounts of ink for short runs can be expensive. Also leftover ink is frequently of no use.

Samples of paper to be printed should be furnished when ordering inks. If this cannot be done, specify what grade the paper will be. However, when printing on a specially treated paper or one that has an unusual printing surface, there is no substitute. In addition, the inkmaker should know the printing process, ink color rotation or sequence, type of press, press speed, drying demands, gloss, varnish, and any special requirements such as alcohol or alkali resistance, fade resistance, etc. *(see Special Characteristics, page 181).*

## LETTERPRESS INKS

Letterpress inks are designed for printing from raised surfaces such as type, engravings and electrotypes. These inks are usually of moderate tack and viscosity. Most letterpress inks for sheet-fed printing dry by oxidation. These are in paste form and consist mainly of pigments and drier ground in a drying-oil vehicle. They may also contain various resins and special compounds to give characteristics such as gloss, scuff-resistance, etc. Letterpress inks for web printing dry by penetration *(newsprint inks),* by evaporation *(heat-set inks),* or by precipitation *(moisture-set inks).* Heat-set inks are formulated with high-boiling, slow-evaporating petroleum oils and solvents. These provide maximum press stability, yet dry rapidly with heat applied in a drier.

## OFFSET-LITHOGRAPHIC INKS

Lithographic inks are formulated to print from planographic surfaces, which utilize the principle that grease and water don't mix. Lithographic inks are generally very strong in color value to compensate for the lesser amount applied. They are the strongest of all inks next to collotype inks. The average amount of ink transferred to the paper is about half that of letterpress because of the double split of the ink film between the plate and the blanket and blanket and paper.

Basically, sheet-fed lithographic inks are similar to letterpress inks of the oxidizing type. However, they contain more water-resistant vehicles and pigments that do not bleed in water or alcohol. Heat-set litho inks are also similar to their letterpress counterparts but use special vehicles and pigments to resist reaction with water and alcohol.

**Letterset inks** have no pigment restrictions to prevent bleeding into a water fountain solution, since letterset does not need any dampening mechanism. Any pigment used for letterpress may be used for letterset. Letterset inks are stronger than letterpress but not as strong as conventional offset inks because the inks are not diluted by emulsified water during running on the press.

## GRAVURE INKS

Gravure inks are rapid-drying fluid inks which must have the proper viscosity to be *pulled* by capillary action from the engraved wells in the cylinder or plate. They dry principally by the evaporation of the solvent in the ink, with or without the use of heat. Gravure inks must be free of abrasive particles that could scratch the engraved cylinder or plate.

A wide variety of solvents are used in gravure depending on the substrate. Most gravure inks are very volatile, and can cause fires or explosions if not handled properly. Solvent recovery is used in many publication plants to eliminate pollution from the evaporated solvents. Water-based inks containing small amounts of alcohol are being developed to eliminate both the fire hazard and solvent pollution.

## FLEXOGRAPHIC INKS

Flexographic inks are fast-drying fluid inks similar in viscosity to gravure inks. They are used in printing almost every kind of surface, from carpeting and wallboard to the various cellophane and plastic films, metal foils, etc. The exceptional color effects afforded by flexography are best exploited by using large masses of color. Flexo inks consist of colorants, which may be either pigments or soluble dyes, together with a vehicle or binder and volatile solvents. They are usually alcohol or water-based although other solvents are also used. Alcohol-base inks are the most common and dry by evaporation. Water-base inks cost less and dry by both evaporation and absorption on paper substrates.

## SCREEN PRINTING INKS

Screen inks are usually of the drying oil type, although others are also used. They have the consistency of thick paint. Inks are made in any color, using a suitable binder for the material to be printed. All inks must be short and buttery to print sharp and squeegee with little resistance. To prevent clogging of the screen, the solvents used should not evaporate too rapidly.

## TYPES OF INKS

Many types of inks are made for different printing uses. Some inks have been developed especially to eliminate starch anti-set-off spray in sheet-fed printing and air pollution from heat-set ink solvents in web printing. Others are used to simulate metallic-luster, print magnetic characters which can be read on special electronic equipment, have alcohol and scuff resistance for liquor labels, alkali resistance for soap packages, and high brilliance for attractive displays.

**Radiation curing inks** have been developed to eliminate spray powder in sheet-fed printing and air pollution from solvents in conventional web heat-set inks. There are two types of these inks: Ultra-Violet (UV) and Electron Beam (EB) curing.

*UV curing inks* consist of liquid prepolymers and initiators which on exposure to large doses of UV radiation release free radicals that polymerize the vehicle to a dry, solid, tough thermosetting resin. Because the active ingredients in these inks are more costly than the solvents they replace in conventional inks, they are expensive (as much as twice the cost of regular inks). Therefore they are not used much in ordinary web printing. They have found use in luxury packaging such as liquor and cosmetic cartons, for metal decorating and screen printing. The total consumption of these inks, however, has been limited by economics. An unexpected shortage of gas or oil, needed to dry heat-set inks, could trigger a conversion to UV inks for web printing but this will be subject to climatic and economic pressures.

*Electron Beam (EB) curing inks* make a good alternative to UV inks since no expensive initiators are needed and some lower cost, less reactive materials can be used. The major disadvantage of EB is the high capital cost of equipping a press to use it. There are several commercial installations of EB on presses with successful results. EB uses less energy than UV which in turn uses about half the energy of gas drying.

**Quick-setting inks** have been very successful for printing on enamel and cast-coated papers in both letterpress and lithography. These inks consist of a delicately balanced oil-resin-solvent vehicle system. Upon contact with the paper under the pressure of printing, the paper surface or coating quickly drains some of the solvents from the ink, yielding a film that sets rapidly and permits handling. Quick-set inks usually dry with a good gloss.

**Super quick-set infrared inks** are a modification of quick-set inks using new synthetic resins with controlled solubility properties used in combination with special blended solvent systems and a minimal amount of drying oils. The setting of these inks is greatly accelerated by the application of heat energy, and IR radiation is a convenient way to apply this energy on a sheet-fed press. Even without heat, these inks set almost 10 times faster than conventional quick-set inks which they are gradually replacing.

**Heat-set inks** are quick-drying inks and are considered one of the most important developments in recent years in web publication printing. The solvents are vaporized as they pass through a heating chamber, leaving the pigment and binding resins fixed to the paper in such a manner that there is no chance for ink spread or excessive penetration into the paper. Presses must be equipped with a heating unit and exhaust system to drive off the solvents, and chill rolls to cool the heated resins.

**High gloss inks** Basically, gloss inks contain an extra quantity of varnish, giving them a glossy appearance when dry. For best results, stocks specially coated for gloss inks should be used. In general, the more resistant the paper is to penetration of the vehicle, the higher the gloss. This property of paper is generally referred to as *holdout*. When heat is used in drying, it has a tendency to reduce gloss. High gloss inks are available for both letterpress and offset.

**Metallic inks** Metallic powders, such as aluminum and copper alloys, mixed with the proper varnish base, give a pleasing metallic luster because the powders are actually flakes which deposit in reflective layers. The bronze powder and vehicle for preparing gold inks are mixed just before using, since the majority of gold inks tarnish rapidly after mixing. The varnish used dries rapidly and has sufficient binding qualities to hold the powder to the paper surface. Coated papers give the best results. On a rough surface paper, however, a base ink is sometimes printed first, allowed to dry, and overprinted with gold. Both aluminum and gold inks can be printed by letterpress, offset or gravure. When printed by offset, alkaline or neutral fountain solutions are usually used to prevent tarnishing of the bronze powder.

**Moisture-set inks** This letterpress ink consists of pigments dispersed in a vehicle composed of a water-insoluble binder dissolved in a water-miscible, or water-receptive solvent, usually a glycol. Upon subjecting the printing to either steam, fine mist or water, the water-miscible solvent picks up some of the water which causes the water-insoluble binder to precipitate out of solution and bind the pigment firmly to the paper. Moisture-set inks are relatively free from odor, making them ideal for food package printing.

**Magnetic inks** In order to increase the speed and efficiency of handling bank checks, magnetic inks were developed. These inks are made with pigments which can be magnetized after printing, and the printed characters are later "recognized" by electronic reading equipment. These inks must be formulated to produce high-grade printing which will meet the rigid requirements of the reading equipment. Makeready and amount of ink must be precise and consistent.

1 2 3 4 5 6 7 8 9 0 ⑆ ⑈ ⑇ ⑉

Each of the ten numbers and four symbols shown above has a distinctive shape which can feed information to a computer, punch a tape, or do any one of a combination of things.

**Scuff-resistant inks** For many years ink manufacturers have been developing new inks that would be sufficiently scuff-resistant for the packaging industry. The inks required for container use must stay bright and appealing despite the shocks and scuffs of shipping and handling. Thanks to continued research, improved scuff-resistant inks of most types are now available.

**Fluorescent inks** Formerly limited to screen printing, new finer grind pigments and greater pigment strength now permit colors to be printed in one impression by letterpress, lithography and gravure. Duotones and even full-color process are now feasible. The naturally bright inks reflect and emit light, making use of ultraviolet light waves which other inks cannot utilize. The semi-transparency of the inks permits overprinting to achieve inter-mediate color tones.

Fluorescent inks must be printed on a white surface and provide maximum brilliance when contrasted with dark sur-rounding hues. They are suited for jobs of a semi-permanent nature, such as labeling, packaging, direct mail, etc.

**Varnish and lacquer** are used over printing for protection as well as gloss. The inkmaker should know that the printing will be lacquered so that he can formulate his inks to be lacquer-resist-ant. Otherwise, the inks are apt to bleed through the varnish or lacquer. The varnish maker must be informed as to the chemical resistances (soaps, acids, etc.), scuff tests, gloss requirements, and other general specifications required of the varnish so that the proper formulation can be selected.

Lacquers are applied off-line on special coating machines. A variety of press-applied varnishes is available. Most are used in-line on standard presses without heat; drying is by oxidation; gloss and other special characteristics are limited as the var-nishes must be compatible with the wet inks.

**Overcoatings** are used in some sheet-fed printing to replace off-line varnishing and eliminate the need for anti-setoff starch sprays. Acrylic type emulsions with water and alcohol and vary-ing degrees of gloss are coated over the wet inks on the image in-line with the printing. The resin coats the ink, while the water or alcohol disperse in the paper. The coatings dry rapidly prevent-ing the wet inks from scuffing or marking while they dry normally. UV clear varnishes are also used as overcoatings. The main disadvantage is the need for an additional unit on the press to apply the coating.

## SPECIAL CHARACTERISTICS

Inks must have other special characteristics to be satisfactory for the variety of uses to which printed matter is subjected. Inks must dry so that they are *rub* and *smudge resistant*. Labels and packaging printing must be *scuff* and *scratch resistant*. Printed matter used for window displays and outdoors requires inks that are *light fast* and *resist fading*. Ink used for soap wrappers must be *alkali resistant* and not bleed with the product. *Alcohol proof-ness,* or resistance to smearing by alcohol, is a must for liquor labels. Wrappers to be hot waxed must have inks that do not bleed in paraffin.

## ENVIRONMENTAL AND ENERGY CONSIDERATIONS

Governmental regulations are severely restricting all solvents commonly used in printing inks from being emitted to the atmosphere without some control method such as incineration or solvent recovery. Especially affected are gravure, flexography and web offset printing. There are also regulations on the discharge of washup solvents in local sewers and disposal of solid wastes which affect ink manufacture in all these processes.

Enforcement of such regulations will stimulate development and use of new radiation cured, chemically reactive, or water-based inks. In addition, increasing costs and decreasing availability of energy sources from fossil fuels such as natural gas and oil, will direct attention of ink manufacturers and printers to alternative methods of ink drying which are more energy efficient. The dominant printing process of the future will be one that will use an imaging material (ink or toner) that is non-toxic, non-flammable, and non-polluting, and at the same time will be reasonable in cost.

# Graphic arts terms

To list all terms connected with the Graphic Arts would fill a book. Many would be too technical and of little value to anyone other than a skilled craftsman. In this section only the must common terms used in Graphic Arts production are defined:

**absorption** *In paper,* the property which causes it to take up liquids or vapors in contact with it. *In optics,* the partial suppression of light through a transparent or translucent material.

**accordion fold** *In binding,* a term used for two or more parallel folds which open like an accordion.

**additive primaries** *In color reproduction,* red, green, and blue. When lights of these colors are added together, they produce the sensation of white light.

**against the grain** Folding or feeding paper at right angles to the grain direction of the paper.

**agate line** A standard of measurement for depth of columns of advertising space. Fourteen agate lines make one column inch.

**airbrush** *In artwork,* a small pressure gun shaped like a pencil that sprays watercolor pigment by means of compressed air. Used to correct and obtain tone or graduated tone effects. *In platemaking,* used with an abrasive-like pumice to remove spots or other unwanted areas.

**anti-halation backing** *In photography,* coating applied to back of film to prevent halation.

**anti-offset spray** *In printing,* dry or liquid spray used on press to prevent wet ink from transferring from the top of one sheet to the bottom of the next sheet.

**antique finish** A term describing the surface, usually on book and cover papers, that has a natural rough finish.

**aperture** *In photography,* lens opening or lens stop expressed as an F/no. such as F/22.

**apochromatic** *In photography,* color-corrected lenses which focus the three colors, blue, green and red, in the same plane.

**art** All illustration copy used in preparing a job for printing.

**ascender** That part of a lower case letter which rises above the main body, as in ''b''.

**author's alterations** *In composition,* changes and additions in the copy after it has been set in type. Often called ''AAs''.

**backbone** The back of a bound book connecting the two covers; also called *spine.*

**backing up** Printing the reverse side of a sheet already printed on one side.

**back lining** A paper or fabric adhering to the backbone or spine in a hardcover book.

**bad break** *In composition,* starting a page or ending a paragraph with a 'widow'.

**base** *In composition,* the metal below the shoulder of a piece of type. *In letterpress,* the metal or wood block on which printing plates are mounted to make them type high.

**basis weight** The weight in pounds of a ream (500 sheets) of paper cut to a given standard size for that grade: 25 x 38 for book papers, 20 x 26 for cover papers, 22½ x 28½ or 22½ x 35 for bristols, 25½ x 30½ for index. E.g., 500 sheets 25 x 38 of 80-lb. coated weighs eighty pounds.

**bearers** *In presses,* the flat surfaces or rings at the ends of cylinders that come in contact with each other during printing (on American presses), and serve as a basis for determining packing thickness.

**bimetal plate** *In lithography,* a plate used for long runs in which the printing image base is copper or brass and the non-printing area is aluminum, stainless steel, or chromium.

**bit** *In computers,* the basic unit of digital information; contraction of BInary digiT.

**black-and-white** Originals or reproductions in single color, as distinguished from multicolor.

**black printer** *In color reproduction,* the black plate, made to increase contrast of neutral tones and detail.

**blanket** *In offset printing,* a rubber-surfaced fabric which is clamped around a cylinder, to which the image is transferred from the plate, and from which it is transferred to the paper.

**bleed** An extra amount of printed image which extends beyond the trim edge of the sheet or page.

**blind embossing** A design which is stamped without metallic leaf or ink, giving a bas-relief effect.

**blind image** *In lithography,* an image that has lost its ink receptivity and fails to print.

**blowup** A photographic enlargement.

**blueprint** *In offset-lithography and photoengraving,* a photoprint made from stripped-up negatives or positives, used as a proof to check position of image elements.

**body** *In inkmaking,* a term referring to the viscosity, or consistency, of an ink. E.g., an ink with too much body is stiff.

**body type** A type used for the main part or text of a printed piece, as distinguished from the heading.

**bold-face type** A name given to type that is heavier than the text type with which it is used.

**bond paper** A grade of writing or printing paper where strength, durability, and permanence are essential requirements; used for letterheads, business forms, etc.

**book paper** A general term for coated and uncoated papers. The basic size is 25 x 38.

**break for color** *In artwork and composition,* to separate the parts to be printed in different colors.

**brightness** *In photography,* light reflected by the copy. *In paper,* the reflectance or brilliance of the paper.

**broadside** Any large advertising circular.

**brochure** A pamphlet bound in booklet form.

**bronzing** Printing with a sizing ink, then applying bronze powder while still wet to produce a metallic lustre.

**bulk** The degree of thickness of paper. *In book printing,* the number of pages per inch for a given basis weight.

**bump exposure** *In photography,* an exposure in halftone photography especially with contact screens in which the screen is removed for a short time. It increases highlight contrast and drops out the dots in the whites.

**burn** *In platemaking,* common term used for plate exposure.

**byte** *In computers,* a unit of digital information, equivalent to one character or eight bits.

**CAD/CAM** Computer Assisted Design/Computer Assisted Makeup or Manufacturing.

**calender rolls** A set or stack of horizontal cast-iron rolls at the end of a paper machine. The paper is passed between the rolls to increase the smoothness and gloss of its surface.

**caliper** The thickness of paper, usually expressed in thousandths of an inch (mils).

**camera-ready** Copy which is ready for photography.

**caps and small caps** Two sizes of capital letters made in one size of type, commonly used in most roman type faces.

**carbon tissue** *In platemaking,* a pigmented gelatin coating on a paper backing which, when sensitized with potassium bichromate and exposed to a continuous-tone positive and either an overall screen or a screen positive of the same subject, becomes the resist for etching gravure plates and/or cylinders.

**case** *In bookbinding,* the covers of a hardbound book.

**cast coated** Coated paper dried under pressure against a polished cylinder to produce a high-gloss enamel finish.

**catching up** *In lithography,* a term which indicates that the non-image areas of a press plate are starting to take ink or scum.

**chalking** *In printing,* a term which refers to improper drying of ink. Pigment dusts off because the vehicle has been absorbed too rapidly into the paper.

**chemical pulp** *In papermaking,* treatment of groundwood chips with chemicals to remove impurities such as lignin, resins and gums. There are two types, sulfite and sulfate.

**circular screen** A circular-shaped halftone screen which enables the camera operator to obtain proper screen angles for color halftones by rotating the screen.

**coated paper** Paper having a surface coating which produces a smooth finish. Surfaces vary from eggshell to glossy.

**coating** *In platemaking,* the light-sensitive polymer or mixture applied to a metal plate. *In printing,* an emulsion, varnish or lacquer applied over a printed surface to give it added protection.

**cold color** *In printing,* a color which is on the bluish side.

**cold type** Type produced by means other than hot metal. *See strike-on composition.*

**collate** *In binding,* the gathering of sheets or signatures.

**collotype** A screenless printing process of the planographic ink-water type in which the plates are coated with bichromated gelatin, exposed to continuous-tone negatives, and are printed on lithographic presses with special dampening.

**color correction** Any method such as masking, dot-etching, re-etching, and scanning, used to improve color rendition.

**color filter** A sheet of dyed glass, gelatin, plastic or dyed gelatin cemented between glass plates, used in photography to absorb certain colors and permit better rendition of others. The filters used for color separation are: blue, green and red.

**color proofs** *See pre-press proofs, progressive proofs.*

**color separation** *In photography,* the process of separating color originals into the primary printing color components in negative or positive form. *In lithographic platemaking,* the manual separation of colors by handwork performed directly on the printing surface. An artist can pre-separate by using separate overlays for each color.

**commercial register** Color printing on which the misregister allowable is within ± one row of dots.

**composing stick** *In composition,* a hand tool in which type is assembled and justified.

**computer, analog** A computer that solves a mathematical problem by using analogs, like density, of the variables in the problem.

**computer, digital** Computer that processes information in discrete digital form.

**computerized composition** An all-inclusive term for the use of computers to automatically perform the functions of hyphenation, justification and page formatting. All typesetting devices have computers in one form or another to allow these functions.

**condensed type** A narrow or slender type face.

**contact print** A photographic print made from a negative or positive in contact with sensitized paper, film, or printing plate.

**contact screen** A photographically-made halftone screen on film having a dot structure of graded density, used in vacuum contact with the photographic film to produce halftones.

**continuous tone** A photographic image which contains gradient tones from black to white.

**contrast** The tonal gradation between the highlights, middle tones, and shadows in an original or reproduction.

**copy** Any furnished material (typewritten manuscript, pictures, artwork, etc.) to be used in the production of printing.

**copyboard** A frame that holds original copy while it is being photographed by the camera.

**copyfitting** *In composition*, the calculation of how much space a given amount of copy will take up in a given size and typeface. Also, the adjusting of the type size to make it fit in a given amount of space.

**copy preparation** *In photomechanical processes,* directions for desired size and other details for illustrations, and the arrangement into proper position of various parts of the page to be photographed for reproduction. *In typesetting*, checking manuscript copy to insure a minimum of changes after type is set.

**cover paper** A term applied to a variety of papers used for the covers of catalogs, brochures, booklets, and similar pieces.

**creep** *In offset,* the forward movement of a blanket during printing. Can also apply to the movement of the packing under the plate or blanket during printing.

**crop** To eliminate portions of the copy, usually on a photograph or plate, indicated on the original by ''cropmarks''.

**cross direction** *In paper,* the direction across the grain. Paper is weaker and more sensitive to changes in relative humidity in the cross direction than the grain direction.

**crossline screen (glass screen)** *In halftone photography,* a grid pattern with opaque lines crossing each other at right angles, thus forming transparent squares or ''screen apertures.''

**crossmarks** *See register marks.*

**CRT** Cathode ray tube—a video display.

**curl** *In paper,* the distortion of a sheet due to differences in structure or coatings from one side to the other, or to absorption of moisture on an offset press.

**curved plate** *In letterpress,* an electrotype or stereotype which is precurved to fit the cylinder of a rotary press.

**cut-off** *In web printing,* the cut or print length corresponding to the circumference of the plate cylinder.

**cutscore** *In die-cutting,* a sharp-edged knife, usually several thousandths of an inch lower than the cutting rules in a die, made to cut part way into the paper or board for folding purposes.

**cyan** One of the subtractive primaries the hue of which is used for one of the 4-color process inks. It reflects blue and green light and absorbs red light.

**cylinder gap** *In printing presses,* the gap or space in the cylinders of a press where the mechanism for plate (or blanket) clamps and grippers (sheet-fed) is housed.

**dampeners** *In lithography,* cloth-covered, parchment paper or rubber (bare back) rollers that distribute the dampening solution to the press plate or ink roller (Dahlgren system).

**dampening system** *In lithography,* the mechanism on a press for transferring dampening solution to the plate during printing.

**dandy roll** *In papermaking,* a wire cylinder on papermaking machines that makes wove or laid effects on the texture, as well as the watermark itself. Used in the manufacture of better grades of business and book papers.

**deckle** *In papermaking,* the width of the wet sheet as it comes off the wire of a paper machine.

**deckle edge** The untrimmed feathery edges of paper formed where the pulp flows against the deckle.

**deep-etch plate** *In offset-lithography,* a positive-working plate used for long runs where the inked areas are slightly recessed below the surface. Plate is declining in use.

**densitometer** *In photography,* a sensitive photoelectric instrument which measures the density of photographic images, or of colors. *In printing,* a reflection densitometer is used to measure and control the density of color.

**density** The degree of darkness (light absorption or opacity) of a photographic image.

**dermatitis** *In lithography,* a skin disease characterized by an itching rash or swelling; caused by photographic developers, chromium compounds and solvents.

**descender** That part of a lower case letter which extends below the main body, as in ''p''.

**desensitizer** *In lithographic platemaking,* making non-image areas of a plate non-receptive to ink through chemical treatment of the metal. Its main ingredient is usually a gum. *In photography,* an agent for decreasing color sensitivity of photographic emulsion to facilitate development under comparatively bright light.

**developer** *In photography,* the chemical agent and process used to render photographic images visible after exposure to light. *In lithographic platemaking,* the material used to remove the unexposed coating.

**diazo** *In photography,* a non-silver coating for contact printing. *In offset platemaking,* a light-sensitive coating used on presensitized and wipe-on plates.

**die-cutting** The process of using sharp steel rules to cut special shapes for labels, boxes and containers, from printed sheets. Die-cutting can be done on either flat-bed or rotary presses. Rotary die-cutting is usually done inline with the printing.

**die-stamping** An intaglio process for the production of letterheads, cards, etc., printing from lettering or other designs engraved into copper or steel.

**diffusion transfer** *In photography and platemaking,* a system, like Polaroid, consisting of a photographic emulsion on which a negative is produced, and a receiver sheet on which a positive of the image is transferred during processing.

**dimensional stability** Ability to maintain size; resistance of paper or film to dimensional change with change in moisture content or relative humidity.

**direct screen halftone** *In color separation*, a halftone negative made by direct exposure from the original on an enlarger or by contact through a halftone screen.

**display type** *In composition*, type set larger than the text, used to attract attention.

**distributing rollers** *In printing presses*, rubber covered rollers which convey ink from the fountain onto the ink drum.

**doctor blade** *In gravure*, a knife-edge blade pressed against the engraved printing cylinder which wipes away the excess ink from the non-printing areas.

**dot** The individual element of a halftone.

**dot etching** *In photography*, chemically reducing halftone dots to increase or reduce the amount of color to be printed. Dot etching negatives increase color; dot etching positives reduce color.

**dot gain** *In printing*, a defect in which dots print larger than they should, causing darker tones or colors.

**draw-down** *In inkmaking*, a term used to describe ink chemist's method of roughly determining color shade. A small glob of ink is placed on paper and drawn down with the edge of a putty knife spatula to get a thin film of ink.

**drier** *In inkmaking*, any substance added to hasten drying.

**driography** *In platemaking*, plates which print without water on the press. They consist of ink on metal for image areas and silicone rubber for non-image areas. Also called *waterless* plates.

**drop-out** Portions of originals that do not reproduce, especially colored lines or background areas (often on purpose).

**dry-up** *See catching up*.

**ductor roller** *In lithography*, the roller in both inking and dampening mechanisms on a press which alternately contacts fountain roller and vibrating drum roller.

**dummy** A preliminary layout showing the position of illustrations and text as they are to appear in the final reproduction. A set of blank pages made up in advance to show the size, shape, form and general style of a piece of printing.

**duotone** *In photomechanics*, a term for a two-color halftone reproduction from a one-color photograph.

**duplex paper** Paper with a different color or finish on each side.

**duplicating film** A film for making positives from positives, and negatives from negatives. Also, *in color reproduction*, a special color film used for making duplicates of color transparencies to size, so they can be stripped together and color separated as a unit.

**dye transfer** *In photography,* a process of producing color prints by tanning photographic emulsions and using them to transfer dye solutions to film or paper coated with gelatin.

**electrophotography** Image transfer systems used in copiers to produce images using electrostatic forces. Electrofax uses a zinc oxide coating; Xerography a selenium surface.

**electrostatic plates** Plates for high speed laser printing using zinc oxide, organic photoconductor or cadmium sulphide (KC) coatings.

**elliptical dot** *In halftone photography,* elongated dots which give improved gradation of tones particularly in middle tones and vignettes—also called *chain dots.*

**em** *In composition,* a unit of measurement exactly as wide and high as the point size being set. So named because the letter ''M'' in early fonts was usually cast on a square body.

**embossed finish** Paper with a raised or depressed surface resembling wood, cloth, leather or other pattern.

**embossing** Impressing an image in relief to achieve a raised surface; either overprinting or on blank paper (called *blind embossing*).

**emulsion side** *In photography,* the side of the film coated with the silver halide emulsion which should face the lens during exposure.

**en** One-half the width of an em.

**enamel** A term applied to a coated paper or to a coating material on a paper.

**english finish** A grade of book paper with a smoother, more uniform surface than machine finish.

**etch** *In photoengraving,* to produce an image on a plate by chemical or electrolytic action. *In offset-lithography,* an acidified gum solution used to desensitize the non-printing areas of the plate; also, an acid solution added to the fountain water to help keep non-printing areas of the plate free from ink.

**exposure** The step in photographic processes during which light produces the image on the light-sensitive coating.

**expanded type** A type whose width is greater than normal.

**facsimile transmission** Process of scanning graphic images to convert them into electric signals which are transmitted to produce a recorded likeness of the original. Also called "fax".

**Fadeometer** An instrument used to measure the fading properties of inks and other pigmented coatings.

**fake-color** *In color reproduction,* producing a color illustration by using one image as a key and making the other separations from it manually.

**fanout** *In printing,* distortion of paper on the press due to waviness in the paper caused by absorption of moisture at the edges of the paper, particularly across the grain.

**feeder** *In printing presses,* the section that separates the sheets and feeds them in position for printing.

**felt side** The smoother side of the paper for printing. The top side of the sheet in paper manufacturing.

**filling in (or filling up)** *In letterpress or offset-lithography,* a condition where ink fills the area between the halftone dots or plugs up (fills in) the type.

**filter** *In color separation photography,* a colored piece of gelatin used over or between the lens. *(See color filter.)*

**fine etching** *In platemaking,* dot etching on metal to correct tone values on photoengravings and gravure cylinders.

**fixing** Chemical action following development to remove unexposed silver halide, to make the image stable and insensitive to further exposure.

**flash exposure** *In halftone photography,* the supplementary exposure given to strengthen the dots in the shadow areas of negatives.

**flat** *In offset-lithography,* the assembled composite of negatives or positives, mostly on goldenrod paper, ready for platemaking. Also, a photograph or halftone that is lacking in contrast.

**flat etching** The chemical reduction of the silver deposit in a continuous-tone or halftone plate, brought about by placing it in a tray containing an etching solution.

**flow** *In printing,* the ability of an ink to spread over the surface of the rollers of a press.

**flush cover** A cover that has been trimmed the same size as the inside text pages.

**flush left (or right)** *In composition,* type set to line up at the left (or right). This page is set flush left *and* right.

**flush paragraph** A paragraph with no indention.

**flying paster** *In web printing,* an automatic pasting device that splices a new roll of paper onto an expiring roll, without stopping the press.

**focal length** *In photography,* the distance from the center of the lens to the image of an object at infinity. At same size, the distance from copy to image is four times the focal length of the lens.

**fog** *In photography,* density in the non-image areas.

**folio** The page number.

**font** *In composition,* a complete assortment of letters, numbers, punctuation marks, etc. of a given size and design.

**form** *In offset,* the assembly of pages and other images for printing. *In letterpress,* type and other matter locked in a chase for printing.

**form rollers** The rollers, either inking or dampening, which directly contact the plate on a printing press.

**format** The size, style, type page, margins, printing requirements, etc., of a printed piece.

**fountain solution** *In lithography,* a solution of water, gum arabic and other chemicals used to dampen the plate and keep nonprinting areas from accepting ink.

**free sheet** Paper free of mechanical wood pulp.

**"f" stops** *In photography,* fixed stops for setting lens apertures.

**fuzz** Fibers projecting from the surface of a sheet of paper.

**galley proof** A proof of text copy before being made into pages.

**gamma** A measure of contrast in photographic images.

**gathering** The assembling of folded signatures in proper sequence.

**gear streaks** *In printing,* parallel streaks appearing across the printed sheet at same interval as gear teeth on the cylinder.

**generation** Each succeeding stage in reproduction from the original copy.

**goldenrod paper** *In offset-lithography,* a specially-coated masking paper of yellow or orange color used by strippers to assemble and position negatives for exposure on plates.

**grain** *In papermaking,* the direction in which most fibers lie which corresponds with the direction the paper is made on a paper machine.

**graining** *In lithography,* subjecting the surface of metal plates to the action of abrasives. Greater water-retention and adhesion of coating is imparted to an otherwise non-porous surface.

**grammage** Term in the Metric System for expressing the basis weight of paper. It is the weight in grams of a square meter of the paper expressed in $g/m^2$.

**gray scale** A strip of standard gray tones, ranging from white to black, placed at the side of original copy during photography to measure tonal range and contrast (gamma) obtained.

**gripper edge** The leading edge of paper as it passes through a printing press. Also, the front edge of a lithographic or wraparound plate that is secured to front clamp of plate cylinder.

**gripper margin** Unprintable blank edge of paper on which grippers bear, usually ½ inch or less.

**grippers** *In printing presses,* metal fingers that clamp on paper and control its flow as it passes through.

**groundwood pulp** A mechanically-prepared wood pulp used in the manufacture of newsprint and publication papers.

**gum arabic** *In offset-lithography,* used in platemaking and on press to desensitize the non-printing areas of plates, and with bichromate to sensitize deep-etch and bimetal plates.

**gumming** *In platemaking,* the process of applying a thin coating of gum arabic to the non-printing areas of a lithographic plate.

**gutter** The blank space or inner margin, from printing area to binding.

**hairline register** Register within ± ½ row of dots.

**halation** *In photography,* a blurred effect, resembling a halo, usually occurring in highlight areas or around bright objects.

**halftone** The reproduction of continuous-tone artwork, such as a photograph, through a crossline or contact screen, which converts the image into dots of various sizes.

**hard copy** The permanent visual record of the output of a computer or printer. Also, the material sent to a typesetter in typed form, for conversion into typeset material.

**hard proof** A proof on paper or other substrate as distinguished from a *soft proof* which is an image on a VDT screen.

**hardware** Computer and peripherals as distinguished from *software* which is program for operating hardware.

**hard dot** *See soft dot.*

**head margin** The white space above first line on a page.

**hickeys** *In offset-lithography,* spots or imperfections in the printing due to such things as dirt on the press, dried ink skin, paper particles, etc.

**high contrast** *In photography,* a reproduction with high gamma in which the difference in darkness (density) between neighboring areas is greater than in the original.

**highlight** The lightest or whitest parts in a photograph represented in a halftone reproduction by the smallest dots or the absence of all dots.

**holdout** *In printing,* a property of coated paper with low ink absorption which allows ink to set on the surface with high gloss. Papers with too much holdout cause problems with set-off.

**hot type** Cast metal type.

**hue** *In color,* the main attribute of a color which distinguishes it from other colors.

**hydrophilic** Water-loving; preferred to be wet by water.

**hydrophobic** Water-hating; water repellent.

**hypo** An abbreviation for sodium thiosulfate, or sodium hyposulfite, a chemical used to fix the image on a photographic film after it has been developed.

**idiot tape** *In computerized phototypesetting,* perforated tape which does not contain codes for hyphenation and justification.

**image assembly** *See stripping.*

**imposition** The arranging of pages in a press form to insure the correct order after the printed sheet is folded and trimmed.

**impression** *In printing,* the pressure of type, plate or blanket as it comes in contact with the paper.

**impression cylinder** *In printing,* the cylinder on a printing press against which the paper picks up the impression from the inked plate in direct printing, or the blanket in offset printing.

**ink fountain** *In printing presses,* the device which stores and supplies ink to the inking rollers.

**ink mist** Flying filaments or threads formed by long inks like newspaper ink.

**Inkometer** An instrument for measuring the tack of printing inks.

**insert** A printed piece prepared for insertion into a publication or another printed piece.

**italic** The style of letters that slant, in distinction from upright, or roman, letters. Used for emphasis within text.

**jog** To align sheets of paper into a compact pile.

**justify** *In composition,* to space out lines uniformly to the correct length.

**kerning** *In typesetting,* subtracting the space between two characters, so that they appear closer together.

**key** To code copy to a dummy by means of symbols, usually letters. Insertions are sometimes "keyed" in like manner.

**keyboard** *In phototypesetting,* the input device to input information directly into a typesetter, or, as a stand-alone unit, to record it on paper or magnetic tape.

**keyline** *In artwork,* an outline drawing of finished art to indicate the exact shape, position, and size for such elements as halftones, line sketches, etc.

**key plate** *In color printing,* the plate used as a guide for the register of other colors. It normally contains the most detail.

**kiss impression** A very light printing impression, just enough to produce an image on the paper.

**kraft** A paper or board containing unbleached wood pulp (brown in color) made by the sulfate process.

**lacquer** A clear coating, usually glossy, applied to a printed sheet for protection or appearance.

**laid paper** Paper with a pattern of parallel lines at equal distances, giving a ribbed effect.

**lamination** A plastic film bonded by heat and pressure to a printed sheet for protection or appearance.

**laser** The acronym for *light amplification by stimulated emission of radiation.* The laser is an intense light beam with very narrow band width that can produce images by electronic impulses. It makes possible imaging by remote control from computers or facsimile transmission.

**laser platemaking** The use of lasers for scanning pasteups and/or exposing plates in the same or remote locations.

**layout** The drawing or sketch of a proposed printed piece. *In platemaking*, a sheet indicating the settings for the step-and-repeat machine.

**leaders** *In composition*, rows of dashes or dots used to guide the eye across the page. Used in tabular work, programs, tables of contents, etc.

**leading** *In composition*, the distance between lines of type measured in points.

**ledger paper** A grade of business paper generally used for keeping records. It is subjected to appreciable wear and requires a high degree of durability and permanence.

**letterset (dry offset)** The printing process which uses a blanket (like conventional offset) for transferring the image from plate to paper. Unlike lithography, it uses a relief plate and requires no dampening system.

**letterspacing** The placing of additional space between each letter of a word.

**line copy** Any copy suitable for reproduction without using a half-tone screen.

**lockup** *In letterpress*, to position a form in a chase for printing.

**logotype (or logo)** The name of a company or product in a special design used as a trademark in advertising.

**long ink** An ink that has good flow on ink rollers of a press. If the ink is too long, it breaks up into filaments on the press, and causes ''flying'' as on a newspaper press.

**lower case** The small letters in type, as distinguished from the capital letters.

**M** Abbreviation for a quantity of 1000 sheets of paper.

**machine coated** Paper which is coated one or two sides on a paper machine.

**machine direction** Same as grain direction in paper.

**magenta** One of the subtractive primaries the hue of which is used for one of the 4-color process inks. It reflects blue and red light and absorbs green light.

**magenta screen** A dyed contact screen, used for making halftones.

**makeover** *In platemaking*, a plate which is remade.

**makeready** *In printing presses,* all work done prior to running, i.e., adjusting the feeder, grippers, side guide, putting ink in the fountain, etc. Also, *in letterpress,* the building up of the press form, so that the heavy and light areas print with the correct impression.

**makeup** *In composition,* the arrangement of lines of type and illustrations into sections or pages of proper length.

**mask** *In color separation photography,* an intermediate photographic negative or positive used in color correction. *In offset-lithography,* opaque material used to protect open or selected areas of a printing plate during exposure.

**master** A plate for a duplicating machine.

**mat** *See matrix.*

**matrix** A mold in which type is cast in linecasting machines. *In stereotyping,* the paper mold or mat made from a type form.

**matte finish** Dull paper finish without gloss or luster.

**matte print** Photoprint having a dull finish.

**measure** *In composition,* the width of type, usually expressed in picas.

**mechanical** *Used mostly in offset,* a term for a camera-ready pasteup of artwork. It includes type, photos, line art, etc., all on one piece of artboard.

**mechanical pulp** *In papermaking,* groundwood pulp produced by mechanically grinding logs or wood chips. It is used mainly for newsprint and as an ingredient of base stock for lower grade publication papers.

**metric system** A decimal system adopted by most other countries for solid, liquid and distance measurements. U.S. will eventually convert. At present the Metric System for paper basis weights is preferred by TAPPI. *(See grammage.)*

**middle tones** The tonal range between highlights and shadows of a photograph or reproduction.

**modem** (MOdulator/DEModulator) A device that converts computer data into high-frequency signals or vice versa, for transmission over phone lines.

**moiré** *In color process printing,* the undesirable screen pattern caused by incorrect screen angles of overprinting halftones.

**molleton** *In offset-lithography,* a thick cotton fabric similar to flannel used on the dampening rollers of a press.

**montage** *In artwork,* several photographs pasted on one art-board in a pleasing manner. They can be placed on angles, overlapped, cut to various shapes, etc.

**mottle** The spotty or uneven appearance of printing, mostly in solid areas.

**mullen tester** A machine for testing the bursting strength of paper.

**Mylar** *In offset preparation,* a polyester film made by DuPont specially suited for stripping positives because of its mechanical strength and dimensional stability.

**negative** *In photography,* film containing an image in which the values of the original are reversed so that the dark areas appear light and vice versa. *(See positive.)*

**newsprint** Paper made mostly from groundwood pulp and small amounts of chemical pulp; used for printing newspapers.

**no-screen exposure** *See bump exposure.*

**oblong** *In binding,* a booklet or catalog bound on the shorter dimension.

**off-press proofs** *See pre-press proofs.*

**offset** *See set-off. In printing,* the process of using an intermediate blanket cylinder to transfer an image from the image carrier to the substrate. Short for offset lithography.

**offset gravure** Printing gravure by the offset principle. Generally done on a flexographic press by converting the anilox roller to a gravure image cylinder and covering the plate cylinder with a solid rubber plate.

**offset/gravure conversions** Use of lithographic positives to produce gravure cylinders.

**opacity** That property of paper which minimizes the "show-through" of printing from the back side or the next sheet.

**opaque** *In photoengraving and offset-lithography,* to paint out areas on a negative not wanted on the plate. *In paper,* the property which makes it less transparent.

**opaque ink** An ink that conceals all color beneath it.

**orthochromatic** Photographic surfaces insensitive to red but sensitive to ultraviolet, blue, green, and yellow rays.

**overhang cover** A cover larger in size than the pages it encloses.

**overlay** *In artwork,* a transparent covering over the copy where color break, instructions or corrections are marked. Also, transparent or translucent prints which, when placed one on the other, form a composite picture.

**overprinting** Double printing; printing over an area that already has been printed.

**overrun** *In printing,* copies printed in excess of the specified quantity.

**overset** *In composition,* type set in excess of space needs in publications, etc.

**packing** *In printing presses,* paper used to underlay the image or impression cylinder in letterpress, or the plate or blanket in lithography, to get proper squeeze or pressure for printing.

**page makeup** *In stripping,* assembly of all elements to make up a page. *In computerized typesetting,* the electronic assembly of page elements to compose a complete page with all elements in place on a video display terminal and on film or plate.

**pagination** *In computerized typesetting,* the process of performing page makeup automatically.

**panchromatic** Photographic film sensitive to all visible colors.

**paper master** A paper printing plate used on an offset-duplicator. The image is made by hand drawing, typewriter or electrophotography.

**paste drier** *In inkmaking,* a type of drier used in inks, usually a combination of drying compounds.

**pasteup** *See mechanical.*

**perfecting press** A printing press that prints both sides of the paper in one pass.

**pH** A number used for expressing the acidity or alkalinity of solutions. A value of 7 is neutral in a scale ranging from 0 to 14. Solutions with values below 7 are acid, above 7 are alkaline.

**photoconductor** Materials used in electrophotography which are light sensitive when charged by corona.

**photomechanical** Pertaining to any platemaking process using photographic negatives or positives exposed onto plates or cylinders covered with photosensitive coatings.

**photopolymer coating** *In photomechanics,* a plate coating consisting of compounds which polymerize on exposure to produce tough abrasion-resistant plates capable of long runs especially when baked in an oven after processing.

**phototypesetting** The method of setting type photographically.

**pica** Printer's unit of measurement used principally in typesetting. One pica equals approximately ⅙ of an inch.

**picking** The lifting of the paper surface during printing. It occurs when pulling force (tack) of ink is greater than surface strength of paper.

**pigment** *In printing inks,* the fine solid particles used to give color, body or opacity.

**piling** *In printing,* the building up or caking of ink on rollers, plate or blanket; will not transfer readily. Also, the accumulation of paper coating on the blanket of offset press.

**pin register** The use of accurately positioned holes and special pins on copy, film, plates and presses to insure proper register or fit of colors.

**plate cylinder** The cylinder of a press on which the plate is mounted.

**plate finish** A smooth, hard finish of paper achieved by calendering.

**point** Printer's unit of measurement, used principally for designating type sizes. There are 12 points to a pica; approximately 72 points to an inch.

**poor trapping** *In printing,* the condition in wet printing in letterpress and lithography when less ink transfers to previously printed ink than to unprinted paper. Also called *undertrapping.*

**porosity** The property of paper that allows the permeation of air, an important factor in ink penetration.

**positive** *In photography,* film containing an image in which the dark and light values are the same as the original. The reverse of negative.

**pre-press proofs** Proofs made by photomechanical means in less time and at lower cost than press proofs. Also called *off-press proofs.*

**presensitized plate** *In photomechanics,* a metal or paper plate that has been precoated with a light-sensitive coating.

**press proofs** *In color reproduction,* a proof of a color subject on a printing press, in advance of the production run.

**pressure-sensitive paper** Material with an adhesive coating, protected by a backing sheet until used, which will stick without moistening.

**primary colors** *See additive primaries, subtractive primaries.*

**print quality** *In paper,* the properties of the paper that affect its appearance and the quality of reproduction.

**process colors** *In printing,* the subtractive primaries: yellow, magenta and cyan, plus black in 4-color process printing.

**process lens** A highly corrected photographic lens for graphic arts line, halftone and color photography.

**process printing** The printing from a series of two or more half-tone plates to produce intermediate colors and shades. In four-color process: yellow, magenta, cyan, and black.

**program** *In computers,* sequence of instructions for a computer. Same as *software.*

**progressive proofs (progs)** Proofs made from the separate plates in color process work, showing the sequence of printing and the result after each additional color has been applied.

**psychrometer** A wet-and-dry bulb type of hygrometer. Considered the most accurate of the instruments practical for industrial plant use for determining relative humidity.

**quad** *In hot metal composition,* blank spacing material less than type high used to fill out lines.

**ragged left** *In typesetting,* type that is justified on the right margin and ragged on the left.

**ragged right** *In typesetting,* type that is justified on the left margin and ragged on the right.

**ream** Five hundred sheets of paper.

**reducers** *In printing inks,* varnishes, solvents, oily or greasy compounds used to reduce the consistency for printing. *In photography,* chemicals used to reduce the size of halftone dots or the density of negative or positive images.

**reflection copy** *In photography,* illustrative copy that is viewed and must be photographed by light reflected from its surface. Examples are photographs, drawings, etc.

**register** *In printing,* fitting of two or more printing images on the same paper in exact alignment with each other.

**register marks** Crosses or other devices applied to original copy prior to photography. Used for positioning negatives in register, or for register of two or more colors in process printing.

**relative humidity (RH)** The amount of water vapor present in the atmosphere expressed as a percentage of the maximum that could be present at the *same* temperature.

**reproduction proof** *In composition*, the proof of a type form for purposes of photographic reproduction.

**reprography** Copying and duplicating.

**resist** *In photomechanics*, a light-hardened stencil to prevent etching of non-printing areas on plates.

**respi screen** A contact screen with 110-line screen ruling in the highlights and 220-line in the middle tones and shadows to produce a longer scale and smoother gradation of tones in the light areas of the copy.

**right-angle fold** *In binding*, a term used for two or more folds that are at 90° angles to each other.

**roller stripping** *In lithography*, a term denoting that the ink does not adhere to the metal ink rollers on a press.

**routing** *In letterpress*, the cutting away of the non-printing areas of a plate.

**rub-proof** *In printing*, an ink that has reached maximum dryness and does not mar with normal abrasion.

**run-around** *In composition*, the term describing type set to fit around a picture or another element of the design.

**runnability** Paper properties that affect the ability of the paper to run on the press.

**running head** A headline or title repeated at the top of each page.

**saddle wire** *In binding*, to fasten a booklet by wiring it through the middle fold of the sheets.

**safelight** *In photography*, the special darkroom lamp used for illumination without fogging sensitized materials.

**scaling** Determining the proper size of an image to be reduced or enlarged to fit an area.

**Scan-a-web** *In web printing*, a rotating mirror arrangement where speed can be varied to match speed of press so image on paper web can be examined during printing.

**scanner** An electronic device used in the making of color and tone corrected color separations.

**score** To impress or indent a mark with a string or rule in the paper to make folding easier.

**screen** *See contact screen and crossline screen.*

**screen angles** *In color reproduction*, angles at which the half-tone screens are placed with relation to one another, to avoid undesirable moiré patterns. A set of angles often used are: black 45°, magenta 75°, yellow 90°, cyan 105°.

**screened print** *In photography,* a print with a halftone screen made from a halftone negative or by diffusion transfer.

**screen ruling** The number of lines or dots per inch on a halftone screen.

**scum** *In offset-lithography,* a film of ink printing in the non-image areas of a plate where it should not print.

**self cover** A cover of the same paper as inside text pages.

**semi-chemical pulp** A combination of chemical and mechanical pulping with properties similar to chemical pulp.

**serif** The short cross-lines at the ends of the main strokes of many letters in some type faces.

**set-off** *In presswork,* when the ink of a printed sheet rubs off or marks the next sheet as it is being delivered. Also called *offset.*

**shadow** The darkest parts in a photograph, represented in a halftone by the largest dots.

**sharpen** To decrease in color strength, as when halftone dots become smaller; opposite of ''thicken'' or ''dot spread''.

**sheetwise** To print one side of a sheet of paper with one form or plate, then turn the sheet over and print the other side with another form using same gripper and side guide.

**short ink** An ink that is buttery, and does not flow freely.

**show-through** *In printing,* the undesirable condition in which the printing on the reverse side of a sheet can be seen through the sheet under normal lighting conditions.

**side guide** On sheet-fed presses, a guide on the feed board to position the sheet sideways as it feeds into the front guides before entering the impression cylinder.

**side wire** *In binding,* to wire the sheets or signatures of a magazine or booklet on the side near the backbone.

**signature** *In printing and binding,* the name given to a printed sheet after it has been folded.

**silhouette halftone** A halftone with all screen background removed.

**sizing** The treatment of paper which gives it resistance to the penetration of liquids (particularly water) or vapors.

**skid** A platform support for a pile of cut sheets.

**slitting** Cutting printed sheets or webs into two or more sections by means of cutting wheels on a press or folder.

**small caps** An alphabet of SMALL CAPITAL LETTERS available in most roman type faces approximately the size of the lower case letters. Used in combination with larger capital letters.

**soft dot** *In photography,* a dot is called 'soft' when the halation or fringe around the dot is excessive. Conversely, when the fringe is so slight as to be barely noticeable and the dot is very sharp, it is called 'hard'.

**soft ink** Descriptive of consistency of lithographic inks.

**soft proof** *See hard proof.*

**software** *See program.*

**spectrum** The complete range of colors in the rainbow, from short wavelengths (blue) to long wavelengths (red).

**spine** *See backbone.*

**spiral binding** A book bound with wires in spiral form inserted through holes punched along the binding side.

**staging** *See stopping out.*

**static neutralizer** *In printing presses,* an attachment designed to remove the static electricity from the paper to avoid ink set-off and trouble with feeding the paper.

**step-and-repeat** *In photomechanics,* the procedure of multiple exposure using the same image by *stepping* it in position according to a predetermined layout.

**stereotype** Duplicate relief plate used extensively for newspaper printing.

**stet** A proofreader's mark, written in the margin, signifying that copy marked for corrections should remain as it was.

**stock** Paper or other material to be printed.

**stone** *In lithography,* formerly used as the plate material. *In letterpress,* the bed on which metal type is leveled and locked up.

**stopping out** *In photomechanics,* application of opaque to photographic negatives; application of special lacquer to protect areas in positives in dot etching; staging of halftone plates during relief etching; protecting certain areas of deep-etched plates so that no ink will be deposited on the protected areas.

**stream feeder** *In printing presses,* a type of feeder that feeds several sheets overlapping each other toward the grippers.

**strike-on composition** Type set by a direct-impression method, or on typewriter composing machines. Also known as cold type.

**strike-through** *See show-through.*

**stripping** *In offset-lithography,* the positioning of negatives (or positives) on a flat (goldenrod) prior to platemaking.

**substance** The weight in pounds of a ream (500 sheets) of paper cut to the standard size (17″ x 22″) for business papers (bond, ledger, mimeograph, duplicator and manifold). E.g., 20 pounds. Similar to basis weight of other grades of paper.

**subtractive primaries** Yellow, magenta and cyan, the hues used for process color printing inks.

**sulphate pulp** Paper pulp made from wood chips cooked under pressure in a solution of caustic soda and sodium sulphide. Known as kraft.

**sulphite pulp** Paper pulp made from wood chips cooked under pressure in a solution of bisulphite of lime.

**supercalendar** *In papermaking,* a calender stack, separate from the papermaking machine, with alternate metal and resilient rolls, used to produce a high finish on paper.

**surprint** *In photomechanics,* exposure from a second negative or flat superimposed on an exposed image of a previous negative or flat.

**tack** *In printing inks,* the property of cohesion between particles; the pulling power or separation force of ink. A tacky ink has high separation forces and can cause surface picking or splitting of weak papers.

**Tackoscope** *See Inkometer.*

**text** The body matter of a page or book, as distinguished from the headings.

**thermo-mechanical pulp** *In papermaking,* made by steaming wood chips prior to and during refining, producing a higher yield and stronger pulp than regular groundwood.

**thirty** Used in newspapers, the symbol ''—30—'' means the end of the story.

**tints** Various even tone areas (strengths) of a solid color.

**tissue overlay** A thin, translucent paper placed over artwork (mostly mechanicals) for protection; used to indicate color break and corrections.

**toner** Imaging material used in electrophotography. *In inks,* dye used to tone printing inks, especially black.

**toning** *See scum.*

**tooth** A characteristic of paper, a slightly rough finish, which permits it to take ink readily.

**transparent** *See show-through.*

**transparent copy** *In photography,* illustrative copy such as a color transparency or positive film through which light must pass in order for it to be seen or reproduced.

**transparent ink** A printing ink which does not conceal the color beneath. Process inks are transparent so that they will blend to form other colors.

**transpose** To exchange the position of a letter, word, or line with another letter, word, or line.

**trapping** The ability to print a wet ink film over previously printed ink. *Dry trapping* is printing wet ink over dry ink. *Wet trapping* is printing wet ink over previously printed wet ink.

**trim marks** *In printing,* marks placed on the copy to indicate the edge of the page.

**twin-wire machine** *In papermaking,* a fourdrinier paper machine with two wires instead of one producing paper with less two-sidedness.

**two-sheet detector** *In printing presses,* a device for stopping or tripping the press when more than one sheet attempts to feed into the grippers.

**two-sidedness** *In paper,* the property denoting difference in appearance and printability between its top (felt) and wire sides.

**type gauge** *In composition,* a printer's tool calibrated in picas and points used for type measurement.

**type high** 0.918 inch; the standard in letterpress.

**undercolor removal (UCR)** *In process multi-color printing,* color separation films are reduced in color in areas where all three colors overprint and the black film is increased an equivalent amount in these areas. This improves trapping and reduces ink costs. It is most important in letterpress printing.

**undercut** *In printing presses,* the difference between the radius of the cylinder bearers and the cylinder body, to allow for plate (or blanket) and packing thickness.

**unit** *In multicolor presses,* refers to the combination of inking, plate and impression operations to print each color. A 4-color press has 4 printing units each with its own inking, plate and impression functions.

**-up** *In printing*, two-up, three-up, etc., refers to imposition of material to be printed on a larger size sheet to take advantage of full press capacity.

**vacuum frame** *In platemaking*, a vacuum device for holding copy and reproduction material in contact during exposure.

**varnish** A thin, protective coating applied to a printed sheet for protection or appearance. *Also, in inkmaking*, it can be all or part of the ink vehicle.

**vehicle** *In printing inks*, the fluid component which acts as a carrier for the pigment.

**vellum finish** *In papermaking*, a toothy finish which is relatively absorbent for fast ink penetration.

**velox** A photographic paper print made from a screen negative.

**video display terminal (VDT)** *In phototypesetting*, a cathode ray tube (CRT) device with keyboard to display copy, make corrections, combine copy elements and perform other typesetting functions.

**vignette** An illustration in which the background fades gradually away until it blends into the unprinted paper.

**viscosity** *In printing inks*, a broad term encompassing the properties of tack and flow.

**walk-off** *In lithography*, deterioration of part of image area on plate during printing.

**warm color** *In printing*, a color with a yellowish or reddish cast.

**washup** The process of cleaning the rollers, form or plate, and sometimes the ink fountain of a printing press.

**watermark** *In papermaking*, a design impressed on paper by the raised pattern of the dandy roll during manufacture.

**web** A roll of paper used in web or rotary printing.

**web press** A press which prints from rolls (or webs) of paper.

**web tension** The amount of pull or tension applied in the direction of travel of a web of paper by the action of a web-fed press.

**whirler** *In platemaking*, a device for applying photosensitive coatings to in-plant coated printing plates in photoengraving, deep etch and bimetal plates. Presensitized and wipe-on plates eliminate the need of a whirler.

**widow** *In composition*, a single word in a line by itself, ending a paragraph; frowned upon in good typography.

**wipe-on plate** *In offset-lithography,* a plate on which a light-sensitive coating is wiped on or applied with a coating machine.

**wire-o binding** A continuous double series of wire loops run through punched slots along the binding side of a booklet.

**wire side** *In papermaking,* the side of a sheet next to the wire in manufacturing; opposite from felt or top side.

**with the grain** Folding or feeding paper into a press parallel to the grain of the paper.

**woodcut** An illustration in lines of varying thickness, cut in relief on plank-grain wood, for the purpose of making prints.

**word processing** Typewriters connected to a form of recording medium to input, revise, and output data.

**work and tumble** To print one side of a sheet of paper, then turn the sheet over from gripper to back using the same side guide and plate to print the second side.

**work and turn** To print one side of a sheet of paper, then turn the sheet over from left to right and print the second side. The same gripper and plate are used for printing both sides.

**wove paper** Paper having a uniform unlined surface and a soft smooth finish.

**wraparound plate** *In rotary letterpress,* a thin one-piece relief plate which is wrapped around the press cylinder like an offset plate. Can be used for direct or indirect (offset) printing.

**wrinkles** Creases in paper occurring during printing. *In inks,* the uneven surface formed during drying.

**wrong font** *In proofreading,* the mark ''WF'' indicates a letter or figure of the wrong size or face.

**yellow** One of the subtractive primaries the hue of which is used for one of the 4-color process inks. It reflects red and green light and absorbs blue light.

**xerography** A copying process that utilizes a selenium surface and electrostatic forces to form an image. *(See electrophotography.)*

# IP printing
# papers

International Paper Company, founded in 1898, today employs over 33,700 men and women in pulp and paper mills and converting plants in the United States and overseas. Behind the people operating these mills and plants is a large woodlands organization which operates the company's forest holdings according to the latest standards of scientific forest management and under the principles of multiple use.

International Paper's numerous and diversified paper products are known and used throughout the world. Most of the fine printing papers, described on the following pages, are distributed nationally by leading paper merchants.

## REPROGRAPHIC PAPERS

**Springhill® Business Paper** is a premium quality multi-purpose paper intended for the full range of office communication uses, including letterheads, price lists, bulletins, and newsletters. Precision-sheeted Springhill Business Paper combines good whiteness, high brightness, opacity, feel, printability, and erasability in a single sheet. It is designed for outstanding performance in today's major reprographic processes—low- and medium-volume xerographic, offset duplicating, mimeo and short-run duplicator.

**Springhill® High-Speed Copy Paper** is a precision-sheeted, bright white, premium quality sheet. This grade offers excellent printability and high-volume performance as a dual purpose sheet. An excellent choice for demanding xerographic and offset duplicator processes.

**IPCO® Business Paper** is a standard quality, bright white, multi-purpose sheet, available in popular cut sizes. IPCO Business Paper gives superior runnability in the major reprographic processes; suitable for low- and medium-volume xerographic, offset duplicating, mimeo and short-run duplicator.

**IPCO® High-Speed Copy Paper** is a precision-sheeted, bright white, dual purpose sheet with outstanding runnability. Economically priced, IPCO High-Speed Copy Paper is suitable for both moderate and high-volume xerographic systems and offset duplicating applications.

**IPCO® Duplicator** is a high quality, bright white sheet, available in popular cut sizes. This sheet is designed specifically for moderate- to high-volume spirit duplicating applications.

## PRINTING BRISTOLS

**Springhill® Vellum Bristol-Cover** is an economical choice for use as a bristol or cover stock. Transparent and opaque inks print easily for beautiful full-color reproductions with remarkable depth and color tone. Its excellent die-cutting, embossing, scoring, and folding qualities make Springhill Vellum Bristol-Cover equally adaptable to menus, greeting cards, catalog inserts, business reply cards, and many other items. Eight colors—plus white—are matched to Springhill Bond/Offset Colors, making Springhill Vellum Bristol-Cover the smart choice for brochures and booklets with matching cover and text pages.

**Springhill® Index** is a truly versatile bristol, noted for its durability, strength, snap and erasability. It is ideal for printed pieces that will require a lot of handling. Springhill Index is made for use in index systems, file cards, file folders, case jackets, covers, menus, die-cut cards, charts, sales kits, and direct mail pieces. Springhill Index comes in six colors, four of which (green, buff, blue, and canary) match Springhill Vellum Bristol-Cover colors.

**Springhill® Tag** The snap, resilience and controlled surface smoothness of Springhill Tag assures excellent runnability whether printed by letterpress, offset, or rotogravure. High tear strength and stiffness permit high-speed production of smooth die-cuts, as well as stamping and embossing. Internal and surface sizing insures the good pen and ink writing properties required by many forms and record card applications. Dependable printability, combined with the benefits of a durable sheet, make Springhill Tag the ideal printing bristol for time cards, ruled forms, menus, folders, catalog inserts and covers, and counter displays. Springhill Tag is stocked in a full range of popular printing sizes and is available in white, manila and six colors.

**Feedcote® C1S** is an economical coated bristol with a smooth finish, designed to lend a quality appearance to halftone reproduction. The coating insures superior ink and varnish holdout. Feedcote scores, diecuts, and folds well, and is particularly suited for promotional folders, direct mail pieces, point-of-purchase displays, sales kits, record jacket covers, tent cards and brochure covers.

## COMMERCIAL PRINTING AND PUBLISHING PAPERS

**Springhill® Offset White** This economically priced wove and vellum finish offset sheet is legendary for its runnability. It has a blue-white shade that pleases the eye in all weights. Brightness and contrast are even more apparent after the sheet is printed. Because the brightness, opacity, and even formation are achieved by using hardwood fibers, not fillers, there's a heft and texture to this fast-drying paper that will last. So will its brightness. Springhill Offset White is used for books, brochures, catalogs, bulletins, direct mail pieces, parts manuals, advertising inserts, and much more.

Springhill Return Postcard is a high bulk offset sheet guaranteed to meet postal regulations for thickness at the lightest practical weight.

**Springhill® Bond/Offset Colors** are suitable for offset, xerographic, mimeo, and duplicator use. It's a sheet designed for the text pages of brochures and reports, booklets, price lists, letterheads, newsletters, direct mail, and much more. The eight Springhill Bond/Offset Colors match the Springhill Vellum Bristol-Cover colors, and four colors of Springhill Index, giving dozens of creative options.

**Bookmark® Book** is IP's answer to publishers' and manufacturers' pleas for lower cost materials. It exceeds NASTA specifications for textbook end-use in all weights, yet offers the economy that only a modern, fully-integrated mill like the Ticonderoga facility will allow. Bookmark leads the IP line of book papers with two shades and standard or custom bulks available in 45–80 lb. weights designed specifically for book end-use. Pleasing in feel and appearance, reliable in web or sheet-fed offset production, carefully produced to the customer's bulk requirement, Bookmark is a traditional book sheet at a not-so-traditional price.

**Springhill® Book** is the best value in a bulking book sheet. Springhill Book is an adaptation of our well-known uncoated offset grade. It is made as a book printer would want it, carefully produced to four standard bulks in each weight (Antique, Eggshell, Standard and English Finish) and in popular 555 cream shade, as well as standard 110 white. This is the low-cost alternative for those jobs that do not require NASTA opacity levels, but still must fit the other needs of the book publisher and manufacturer.

**Springhill® Book-Belt Press** is IP's belt press adaptation of Springhill Book. Springhill Book-Belt Press has the dimensional stability and uniform high bulk best suited to Cameron belt press work. It is available in 55 lb. basis weight, antique finish (330 PPI) and two shades: cream and standard white.

**Bookmark® Endleaf** is a strong, rugged sheet for the most demanding use in book-binding. Bookmark Endleaf meets the standards established by NASTA. Its fold endurance and bright white finish provide the performance, as well as the appearance the book publisher wants. Designed to be readily glued, it also is suitable for offset or letterpress overprinting.

**Publication Gloss®** publication paper is a favorite for economy and outstanding coating, making it the choice for many well-known publications, catalogs and advertising pieces. This No. 5 coated two sides sheet is made for either letterpress or gravure. It is designed to have a smooth surface and good ink holdout.

**Educator® II** publication paper is a No. 4 quality dull coated groundwood book paper. It can be produced in lower basis weights without sacrificing opacity or bulk. Good printability, brightness and cleanness with additional characteristics such as fine texture, feel, good ink holdout and dependable printability make Educator an ideal book publishing grade. This grade meets NASTA specifications for use in EL-HI textbooks.

**Educator® Thin** publication paper is also a No. 4 quality dull sheet and is lightly supered to give it unusual bulking characteristics. Although this grade does not meet NASTA specifications, it is well suited for use in reference books and college textbooks.

**Hudson® Web Gloss** is a superior coated grade, available in gloss finish. This No. 5 coated two sides sheet is designed to have good ink holdout in addition to water and pick resistance. It provides excellent reproduction for various web offset printing requirements. Suitable for magazines, newspaper inserts, coupons and catalogs.

**Hudson® Web Dull** is an unsupered version of Hudson Web Gloss. This matte finish groundwood sheet is used successfully on coupon inserts for Sunday newspapers.

**Hudson® Workbook** is a groundwood coated grade available in dull (matte) finish manufactured without the supercalender process. Designed specifically for end-use in school workbooks.

**IP Web® Gloss** is a No. 4 coated web offset sheet with a gloss finish designed for good water and pick resistance, as well as excellent reproduction. Used in catalogs, trade publications and direct mail. High brightness is suited to large unprinted areas such as editorial pages.

**Springhill® Web Gloss** is our premium quality No. 4 coated publication grade. Higher opacity, brightness and strength due to groundwood. This grade resembles a free sheet and is used for high quality catalogs, brochures, magazines, and direct mail.

## ADDITIONAL IP PAPERS AND BOARDS

### Free Sheet Converting and Specialty Grades

Envelope Paper—White Wove and Kraft
Tablet Paper
Data-Speed® Form Bond
Carbonizing Tissue
Adding Machine Paper
Placemat Paper
Wallboard Tape
File Folder
Tabulating Index
OCR Papers
Label Papers
Label Release Paper
Detail Paper

® Registered trademark of International Paper Company.

Cover: Feedcote®, C1S 10-pt. Text: Bookmark®, Blue-White, 60 lb.
Cover photo: Laszlo Studio, Inc., N.Y.C.

Printed in U.S.A.